THE L
CHRISTOPHE

A Comedy in Three Acts

An English Adaptation of

RENÉ FAUCHOIS'S

Prenez Garde à la Peinture!

BY

EMLYN WILLIAMS

SAMUEL FRENCH

LONDON
NEW YORK TORONTO SYDNEY HOLLYWOOD

THE LATE CHRISTOPHER BEAN

Produced at the St. James's Theatre, London, S.W.1, on May 15th, 1933, with the following cast of characters :

(In the order of their appearance)

DR. HAGGETT	*Cedric Hardwicke.*
SUSAN HAGGETT	*Lucille Lisle.*
GWENNY	*Edith Evans.*
MRS. HAGGETT	*Louise Hampton.*
ADA HAGGETT	*Nadine March.*
BRUCE McRAE	*Barry K. Barnes.*
TALLANT	*Robert Holmes.*
ROSEN	*Clarence Derwent.*
DAVENPORT	*Frederick Leister.*

The Play produced by GILBERT MILLER.

SYNOPSIS OF SCENERY

The Scene is laid in the living-room of " The Old House," the Haggetts' home in Childer Barnston, a small village somewhere near the centre of England.

ACT   I.—Morning.

ACT II.—Noon.

ACT III.—Afternoon.

The time is the present. A day in May.

THE LATE CHRISTOPHER BEAN

ACT I

SCENE.—*The living-room of the* HAGGETTS' *home in Childer Barnston.*
TIME.—*About* 9.30 *a.m., on a bright sunny May morning.*
*The house is old, and the room is worthy of more tasteful furnishing
than the Haggett family has given it. Mingled with the few old
pieces is much of less merit, very genteel and rather overcrowded.
Added to this are the desk, medical cabinet and other furnishings,
which have been moved in from the Doctor's surgery. The room is
used as both living- and dining-room, and there is a round dining-
table* R.C. *with four chairs, also a sideboard against the wall* R.
*These pieces of furniture give the room away for what it is. A bay-
window, with lace curtains, overlooks the village road, and in the
bay is a large aspidistra on a stand. Through the double-doors up*
C., *which are open, one gets a glimpse of the passage leading to the
front door. In the passage is a step-ladder, paint-cans and brushes,
and a crude sign on the stair newel-post, which reads* " WET PAINT."
A door down R. *leads to the kitchen.*
(See Photograph of Scene, also Furniture and Property Plot.)

The CURTAIN *rises on an empty stage. After a moment of silence
the front door opens to admit* DR. HAGGETT, *an undistinguished,
tired-looking medical man of fifty ; he is the typical English country
doctor, his gentility (born of grammar-school education) slightly worn
by years of contact with rustic patients. He removes his old Derby
hat and shabby overcoat and hangs them on a peg in the hall, just
off* L. *He is wearing old striped trousers, a shabby morning-coat
and vest, a white shirt, and a wing collar with grey pattern tie.
When he is standing up his trousers sag over his grey spats and
black boots.*

DR. HAGGETT (*in the hall, calling*). Hannah !
MRS. HAGGETT (*upstairs*). Is that you, Arthur ?
DR. HAGGETT. Yes, it is.
MRS. HAGGETT. Are you back already ?
DR. HAGGETT. Yes, I am. (*He enters the room.*)
MRS. HAGGETT. Have you had your breakfast ?
DR. HAGGETT. No, I haven't. (*He goes to his desk and puts his
bag on it.*)

MRS. HAGGETT (*still upstairs, calling loudly*).   Gwenny !

(*Something on* DR. HAGGETT'S *hands annoys him.   Smelling them, he gets a strip of gauze from a glass jar on the desk and goes to the medical cabinet up* R.C. *that contains his drugs.*)

(*Calling.*)   Gwenny !

(DR. HAGGETT *takes a bottle from the cupboard and proceeds to clean his hands with the contents, drying them with the gauze.*)

(*Calling.*)   Gwenny ! ! !   Get the Doctor his breakfast !   He hasn't had any !

(SUSAN HAGGETT, *a pretty girl of nineteen, comes downstairs.*)

(*Calling.*)   Susan, help Gwenny to get your father's breakfast ready, will you ?

SUSAN (*coming into the room*).   All right.

(DR. HAGGETT *throws the piece of gauze into the fire.*)

MRS. HAGGETT.   Gwenny !

DR. HAGGETT.   Why should Gwenny need any help in getting my breakfast ready ?

SUSAN.   Oh, Gwenny's so upset. . . .   (*She crosses to the table and picks up the bowl of flowers.*)

DR. HAGGETT.   What's upsetting her ?

SUSAN.   Why, Daddy, leaving us !

(*She crosses with the flowers and puts them on the sideboard, then takes the cruet and marmalade from the sideboard cupboard and puts them on the top.*)

DR. HAGGETT (*crossing to the desk*).   Oh yes, of course. . . . To-day *is* Thursday !   Went clean out of my head.   After all the chitter-chatter there's been about it, too. . . .   So Gwenny's leaving us, after all these years !

(*He is looking towards the kitchen door as* GWENNY *enters, carrying a tin tray with teapot, cup and saucer, milk and sugar, and napkin. She wears a smile that decreases in plausibility as it increases in determination.   She is* MRS. HAGGETT'S *maid-of-all-work, a Welsh villager, aged vaguely between youth and maturity, of a wistful prettiness, simple and serious.   She speaks with a soft and pleasing North Wales accent.   She is wearing a white apron over her print morning dress, black shoes with straps, and black stockings.*)

GWENNY.   I got your tea all ready, Doctor Haggett, and it iss lovely and hot and all.

(DR. HAGGETT *sits at the desk.*)

Dear me, to think of you being out all this time on an empty stomach ! Did everything turn out all right ?

DR. HAGGETT. It did, Gwenny. A boy, eight pounds three ounces, turned out.

GWENNY (*setting the tray on the table*). Well, dear me, issn't that a grand thing, now ? I bet you that Mistar and Mrs. Elliott are that pleased because it iss a boy ! I expect most fathers and mothers would sooner have boys than girls by far, and if you ask me, Doctor Haggett, I don't blame them, neither. . . . You just sit there, Doctor Haggett, and Susan, you pour your father's tea out the time that I finish with getting his breakfast. (*Pointing to the newspaper and telegram lying on the table.*) There iss his " Chester Chronicle " all ready for him, and all. And there's a telegram with it that just come.

(*She goes into the kitchen.* SUSAN *pours out tea.*)

DR. HAGGETT (*rising and crossing for the telegram*). She seems to be making quite an effort for the last day. (*He opens the telegram.*)

SUSAN. Well, it's only natural, isn't it, Daddy ? (*She goes to the sideboard.*) It's going to be like losing one of the family. . . . (*As he exclaims.*) What is it, Daddy ? (*She comes back to the table.*)

DR. HAGGETT. It's from London.

SUSAN (*bending over the telegram*). No !

DR. HAGGETT. Yes, it is. (*Reading.*) " An admirer of the late Christopher Bean will do himself the honour of calling on you on Thursday at twelve, noon." Signed, Maxwell Davenport. (*He sits on the chair* L. *of the table.*)

SUSAN (*thoughtfully*). Chris Bean.

DR. HAGGETT. I haven't thought of him for years.

SUSAN (*crossing to the sideboard*). Chris Bean, the boy who painted all those pictures. (*She comes to the table with cruet and marmalade.*)

DR. HAGGETT. You mean, *he* thought they were pictures, when he wasn't too drunk to think ! . . . But who's Maxwell Davenport ? I never heard of him. I don't know if he expects me to know him, but I certainly don't. . . . (*He puts away the telegram in his left coat pocket and takes the tea which* SUSAN *has poured out for him.*)

(MRS. HAGGETT *comes downstairs. She is a thin, shrewd woman of fifty ;* DR. HAGGETT *has married slightly beneath him, but she has assumed certain " cityfied " airs in dress and bearing, and a certain over-refinement of speech ; these, she feels, lift her above the standards of Childer Barnston. She is the complaining sort. She wears a tweed skirt and blouse.*)

(SUSAN *sits* R. *of the table.*)

MRS. HAGGETT (*out in the hall, distastefully viewing the débris in the passage*). Arthur, why hasn't that painter and paper-hanger man taken his rubbish home ? (*She picks up the two paint-cans and puts them down by the step-ladder, then takes the end of the trailing canvas and tucks it on the floor under the ladder.*) He'd finished his work when he went home last night, and he promised faithfully he'd be here first thing this morning. . . . (*Coming into the room.*) Oh dear, (*crossing to above the table*) I do hope we don't have any more painters in the house ! It may interest you to know, Susan, that your poor sister is in bed with a headache the smell of that paint has given her. . . . (*Sitting on the chair above the table.*) When I think of the work that's facing us in this house to-day, moving your father's things back into his study . . . oh, dear . . .

(GWENNY *returns from the kitchen with a tray containing the rest of* DR. HAGGETT'S *breakfast, including porridge. She puts the tray on the downstage end of the sideboard.*)

GWENNY. Here you are for you, Doctor Haggett.

MRS. HAGGETT (*still plaintive*). And Gwenny leaving us this afternoon . . . ah, well . . .

GWENNY. If you got no objection, like, Mrs. Haggett, please, I would prefer for you not to speak about me leaving. (*She gives the bowl of porridge to* DR. HAGGETT.)

MRS. HAGGETT. Well, you are leaving, aren't you ?

GWENNY (*crossing to the sideboard*). Yes, I am leaving. But you know that I don't want to be leaving, and I wouldn't be leaving, neither, only it iss the will of God. (*She puts a jug of hot water on the table.*) And the only way I can keep up my spirits with me leaving, iss for nobody to speak to me about it. But if you keep on at me about it, I . . . (*She crosses to the sideboard.*)

(MRS. HAGGETT *looks up.* SUSAN *lays a warning hand on her mother's arm.* GWENNY *controls herself and smiles bravely.*)

(*Putting a toast-rack on the table.*) What I want to hear about, Mrs. Haggett, if you please, is Mrs. Elliott's baby. She didn't get married none too soon, did she ? My opinion iss that when a baby comes as quick as that after a wedding, you very near have to brush the rice off it. (*Crossing to the sideboard.*) Wass it a long job with the baby, Doctor Haggett ? (*She puts sugar sifter on the table.*)

DR. HAGGETT. Not very long, Gwenny. (*He has begun his breakfast.*)

GWENNY. Oh, I am sure she suffered terrible, issn't it, Doctor Haggett ? You look ready to drop, your own self. It can't have be more than four o'clock when they knock you up. It seems ass if babies iss always getting you up or keeping you up, one of the two, issn't it, Doctor Haggett ?

(ADA HAGGETT, *a girl of twenty-six, who fancies her baby prettiness and baby-like manner, comes slowly downstairs.*)

Susan (*putting her arm round* Gwenny's *waist*). If you feel so very sorry to leave us, Gwenny, why don't you stay ?

Gwenny. Oh, you are all so good to me ! I don't want to go. It is the will of God.

Dr. Haggett. First time I heard of the will of God sending a woman off to live in Manchester.

(Ada *enters and remains standing* l. *of the medical cabinet.*)

Gwenny. But it must have been the will of God to make my poor brother Idwal's wife get poorly, and die, and leave him with four little children, and no woman in the house ! You know that it would not be like your Gwenny to will a thing like that !

Dr. Haggett. Now, Gwenny, don't let us go over it all again, please ! You're leaving us. We're deeply sorry to see you go, but we'll save our tears till the time comes for you to catch your train. By the way, what train *are* you catching ? (*He gives the newspaper to* Mrs. Haggett, *who begins to read.*)

Gwenny. The five o'clock to Chester, from Rocklands Station.

Susan. We're going to miss you, Gwenny !

Gwenny. And what about me, Miss Susan ? What about me leaving this place, where I been for so long ? Fifteen years I been here, fifteen years, mark you !

Dr. Haggett. Don't harp on it.

Gwenny (*turning and crossing to the kitchen door*). I don't want to harp on it, neither, only I cannot bear—really——

(*She goes into the kitchen.*)

Susan (*rising*). Poor Gwenny ! We'll never get another servant like her.

(*She follows* Gwenny *out, closing the door behind her.*)

Dr. Haggett. Well, that wouldn't be a bad idea !

(Mrs. Haggett *looks up from the paper.*)

Mrs. Haggett. Are you suggesting, Arthur, that I should do without a servant ?

Dr. Haggett. I don't see why not. Three women in the house. I'll undertake to make my own bed.

Ada (*moving down a step*). But, Daddy, have you thought what people would say in Church on Sunday ?

Dr. Haggett. Well, what would they say ?

Mrs. Haggett. They'd say Doctor Haggett's practice had fallen into such straits that he couldn't afford to keep a servant.

Dr. Haggett. You look after your house, Hannah, and I'll look after my practice. (*He folds his napkin.*)

Mrs. Haggett. If it weren't for me, you'd sit by the fire all day and let everything go to rack and ruin ! How long did I have to keep on at you, to get your surgery painted and papered ? And that hall, too !

DR. HAGGETT.   It isn't a hall.   It's a passage.

MRS. HAGGETT.   It's a hall.

DR. HAGGETT (*peace at any price*).   All right.   (*He sips his tea.*)

MRS. HAGGETT (*her voice rising*).   Which of us two was it found we could sell that old wallpaper for more than enough to give you a nice clean surgery your patients could enjoy ?

DR. HAGGETT.   I know, I know . . .

MRS. HAGGETT.   And now you want to spoil the whole effect by making your wife and daughters do their own work !   The idea ! (*She returns to the newspaper.*)

DR. HAGGETT.   I know——   And if you could find some way to make my patients pay the bills they owe me . . .

MRS. HAGGETT.   If people won't pay you, then don't attend them.   (*She reads the newspaper.*)

DR. HAGGETT.   And what'ld happen to my practice then ?

MRS. HAGGETT.   Oh, it's no use talking to you . . .   (*She puts the paper on the table.*)

DR. HAGGETT.   A doctor is morally bound to minister to the sick, even if the sick can't pay their bills.   It's the ones who can pay, and don't, these days——

MRS. HAGGETT (*quietly*).   Ada, you'd better go upstairs, dear. I see I must have a private talk with your father.

(ADA *starts to go upstairs, but stops and listens.   DR. HAGGETT puts his glasses in his waistcoat pocket, rises, crosses to the desk, then takes his pouch and pipe from his coat pocket.*)

DR. HAGGETT (*filling his pipe*).   If you could find a new servant for the same wages we pay Gwenny . . .

(MRS. HAGGETT *resumes perusal of the newspaper.*)

MRS. HAGGETT.   The new one I found won't cost us much more.

(DR. HAGGETT *stops and turns to her.*)

DR. HAGGETT.   You don't mean to say you've hunted up a new servant already !

MRS. HAGGETT.   Yes, I have.   Last week, when I went shopping in Blackpool.

DR. HAGGETT.   You found a new servant in Blackpool !

MRS. HAGGETT (*putting the paper down on the table*).   Don't you understand, Arthur, it's in bad times like the present that you've got to keep up appearances most of all ?

(*He sits in the chair at the desk.   She rises and goes to him, on his* R.)

I'm not sorry to see Gwenny leaving, either.   She's been here long enough.   (*As* DR. HAGGETT *butts in.*)   Yes, Arthur, I know what you're going to say—that it's a pleasant homely sight to see her behaving like one of the family, and calling the girls by their Christian names.

(DR. HAGGETT *picks up the tobacco-jar from the desk and fills his pouch.*)

But you know, dear, she hasn't got an atom of style about her! Now, the new one isn't a bit like that. She's a real maid, and smacks of the town, if you know what I mean. And she has a really nice accent, quite grammatical, too; and she answers the door as if to the manner born!

DR. HAGGETT (*looking up at* MRS. HAGGETT). How much does she cost?

MRS. HAGGETT. Now what you have to think about is the money the girls and I are saving by making all our own clothes for the Isle of Man this summer!

DR. HAGGETT (*sitting back, his glance sharpening*). Oh, you're still talking about the Isle of Man this summer, are you?

MRS. HAGGETT (*flustered*). And why . . . shouldn't . . . I?

DR. HAGGETT. Because the girls and you are not going to the Isle of Man, or any other isle, till times get better!

(ADA *bursts in from upstairs.*)

ADA. Did I hear Daddy say we're not going to the Isle of Man? (*She is now* L. *of the table.*)

DR. HAGGETT (*turning in his chair*). Yes, you did, Ada. And not for the first time, either. Perhaps I do sit on one side, and let your mother paint and paper my surgery, perhaps your mother is going to have a servant from Blackpool. Perhaps! But as long as I can't collect the bills my patients owe me, it's no use talking to me about the Isle of Man. . . . I'm sticking to that, as firm as a rock. (*He swings round to face the desk again, and replaces the tobacco-jar.*)

MRS. HAGGETT. And I'm sticking too, and I wouldn't be a mother if I didn't!

DR. HAGGETT. What's being a mother got to do with the Isle of Man?

MRS. HAGGETT. Perhaps you don't care whether your daughters get married or not, but I do!

ADA. And so do they!

DR. HAGGETT. Well, they don't have to go to the Isle of Man to get married.

ADA (*flustered*). Perhaps not, but the opportunities up there are exceptional!

(MRS. HAGGETT *nods her head in agreement.*)

DR. HAGGETT (*irritably*). Rubbish and fiddlesticks, my dear girl, fiddlesticks and rubbish!

MRS. HAGGETT. It isn't rubbish, Arthur, or fiddlesticks either! Do you know, I've heard that in Douglas in the summer time the promenade is simply alive with young men who don't think of anything else but romance and getting married.

DR. HAGGETT. Young men get those ideas anywhere.

MRS. HAGGETT. Not in the north of England in the winter. (*She sits in the armchair* L.C.)

ADA (*moving to* R. *of* MRS. HAGGETT). Daddy wants me to grow up an old maid.

DR. HAGGETT. I didn't say anything of the kind.

ADA (*moving to* DR. HAGGETT). I'm nearly an old maid as it is. . . .

DR. HAGGETT. You're only a baby.

ADA (*turning away*). I'm twenty-four.

DR. HAGGETT (*turning and looking at* ADA). You're twenty-six.

ADA (*sitting on the chair* L. *of the table, her back to* DR. HAGGETT). That makes it all the worse !

DR. HAGGETT. Well, if you're in such a hurry to get married, why don't you go down to Barnston Church and get the vicar to put up an S O S in the vestry ?

ADA (*turning to him*). Oh, Daddy !

MRS. HAGGETT. Really, Arthur, after all the advantages we've given our daughters—Rossborough Girls' School, and everything—do you want to see them married to village lads from Childer Barnston ?

DR. HAGGETT (*speaking out to front*). What's the matter with village lads ? You married one.

MRS. HAGGETT. I hadn't been to the Isle of Man.

(*There is a short pause.*)

DR. HAGGETT (*looking at* MRS. HAGGETT). Thank you, Hannah. Thank you very much. After all the advantages my father gave me, too—Exfield Grammar School, and everything. . . . If Ada can do half as well for herself as you did——

ADA. There aren't any boys to speak of in this place. And what boys there are, don't like me.

DR. HAGGETT. And what is it makes boys in the Isle of Man like you any better ? Is it because they've seen you in a bathing-dress ? All right then, give the Barnston boys a chance. Invite them in here, put your bathing-dress on, and sit by the fire !

(SUSAN *comes in from the kitchen and goes to the chair* R. *of the table.*)

MRS. HAGGETT (*rising and crossing to the chair above the table*). Well, your father's got the better of us again. No Isle of Man for us this summer. I'll have to go into Chester and get Madame Eugenia to take back my artificial silk. (*She sits on the chair above the table.*)

SUSAN (*cheerfully*). Oh, Mummy, what a pity ! But I don't see that it matters very much. (*She sits on the chair* R. *of the table.*)

ADA. It does matter! It does! Daddy says I'm only a baby, but what he really wants is for me to grow up an old maid!

DR. HAGGETT (*rising and moving to* C., *muttering to himself*). I don't want any such thing . . . I . . .

ADA (*facing* MRS. HAGGETT, *her voice rising*). If we stay in Childer Barnston, Susan will get married before me, because the boys here like her better than me, and if she gets married before me, I'll just die . . . I'll die! I know I'll die! (*She sobs and buries her head in her arms on the table.*)

MRS. HAGGETT (*rising to above* ADA *and patting her on the shoulder*). It's this everlasting having just enough, and not a scrap left over for——

DR. HAGGETT (*sorrowfully*). Greed, Hannah! Greed! (*He moves up* C., *then returns to* L. *of the table.*)

MRS. HAGGETT (*furiously*). Perhaps I am greedy! But it's only fools and wasters that don't try to get everything they can out of life.

(GWENNY *comes in from the kitchen, her eye cocked maliciously. She goes to the sideboard and gets the empty tray.*)

DR. HAGGETT. No man has ever called me greedy for money, Hannah. And I hope no man ever does. I'll go upstairs now and shave.

(*He exits up the stairs.* MRS. HAGGETT *starts to follow him, but stops when* GWENNY *speaks.*)

GWENNY. Well, dear me, people are funny, they are really! (*She comes above the table with the tray and starts clearing.*) There iss me crying and breaking my heart over going away, and now you are doing the very same thing egzackly because you got to stay!

MRS. HAGGETT. That's quite enough, Gwenny Thomas. We don't want any observations or remarks.

GWENNY. Oh, Mrs. Haggett, don't mind me! I am only a servant from that terrible country Wales; and I have not got an atom of style about me, and I call the girls by their Christian names, like I was one of the family. And now you got a real maid from Blackpool, and she smacks of the town, yes indeed! And she know how to answer the door-bell like a proper English lady. (*She carries the filled tray to the downstage end of the sideboard.*)

MRS. HAGGETT (*coming to above* L. *of table, furious*). You're a common, impudent girl, Gwenny Thomas, and I give you notice for listening at keyholes!

(BRUCE *crosses the window.*)

GWENNY. You cannot give me notice, because I give myself notice already. And I won't go, till my time iss ripe!

MRS. HAGGETT. I'll take no more back answers from you . . .
you go now !
GWENNY. I go this afternoon.

(BRUCE McRAE, *the village painter and paper-hanger, has come into
the hall from the front door. He is a personable, self-satisfied youth
in his early twenties. He is dressed in a very old paint-smeared
tweed coat, old grey-flannel trousers, and a muffler hiding an open
shirt-front. He speaks with a Scottish accent.*)

BRUCE (*in the doorway*). Good morning, Mrs. Haggett.
MRS. HAGGETT (*turning*). Oh, it's the paper-hanger. . . .
BRUCE. Good morning, Ada. Good morning, Susan.

(*The girls return his greetings.*)

MRS. HAGGETT. I was just saying it's about time you turned up.
GWENNY. Bruce issn't so late that you have to have a fit about
it.
MRS. HAGGETT (*swinging round to her again*). Gwenny Thomas !
BRUCE. In fact, not late at all. Didn't ye know, Mrs. Haggett,
that us folk frae the North, we're never behind for business appoint-
ments ?
MRS. HAGGETT. And never behind for boasting, either.
GWENNY. Bruce iss all right, even tho' he iss Scotch.
MRS. HAGGETT. Well, I'm tired of hearing two such outlandish
accents in my house, (*crossing to* R. *of* BRUCE) and will you please
get your rubbish out of here !
BRUCE (*placidly*). The weather's quite sharp for the time of
year, Mrs. Haggett—summer on the way, too !
MRS. HAGGETT (*with dignity*). Please hurry up. I'm sick of
the smell of paint.
GWENNY (*picking up her tray and starting for the kitchen*). There
iss plenty of things in this house that smells worse than paint.

(*She goes into the kitchen and shuts the door.*)

BRUCE (*still placid*). That's what I've come for, Mrs. Haggett,
to get my rubbish out of here. And I brought for each of ye girls
a wee present.
ADA. A present, Bruce ? One that you paid for ?
BRUCE. Well, hardly that. Ye see, I brought, for each of ye,
one of my pictures. (*He comes down to* L. *of the table and produces
two small framed oil paintings of still life, from under his arm.*)
SUSAN (*rising, delighted*). Bruce !
ADA. A picture of you, Bruce ?
BRUCE. No, not pictures of me. Pictures that I painted. (*He
hands a picture to each of the girls.*)

(MRS. HAGGETT *comes down to* L. *of the table, behind* ADA, *and examines the latter's picture.*)

MRS. HAGGETT. It's a dead fish.

SUSAN (*leaning over to see*). It looks like the salmon you caught on Sunday, Bruce.

BRUCE. Aye, that's what it is.

MRS. HAGGETT. On Sunday, Mr. McRae, when you ought to be in church !

BRUCE. Yes, Mrs. Haggett.

MRS. HAGGETT. You ought to be ashamed . . . (*Turning to* SUSAN.) What's yours, Susan ? . . .

(SUSAN *tilts her picture for them to see*.)

A dead duck ! You'd better change with your sister, Susan. Fish always brings Ada out in a rash.

ADA. Oh, Mummy, not in pictures ! (*With a too ingratiating smile.*) And are they your own work, Bruce ?

(SUSAN *sits on the chair* R. *of the table*.)

BRUCE. They are indeed.

ADA. The frames as well ?

(MRS. HAGGETT *moves up a few steps and crosses* L.)

BRUCE. Aye. They are first-class paintings. I thought to meself ye would perhaps want to hang them over ye sideboard. (*He points to the wall* R.) I thought to meself they would look kind of good for it.

MRS. HAGGETT. But I wouldn't have any appetite if I had to look up at a dead fish and a dead duck ! (*She goes to the desk and arranges papers.*)

ADA. No, Bruce's right, Mummy. They'd look really lovely. (*Flattering.*) To think I never knew you were a picture painter, Bruce !

BRUCE (*blandly*). It seems as if all kinds of painting come natural to me.

ADA. Oh, I can see that ! Oh, Mummy, fancy Bruce ! I'd no idea he was so clever. And I certainly never thought Barnston boys were as interesting as this !

BRUCE. They're not. And ye could hardly call me a Barnston boy, Ada, for I never comes over the border frae Scotland till the age of ten.

ADA. Well, we think of you as one, anyway. . . . Why, you could paint really fine pictures if you took to studying ! I'm only a baby, but I used to take painting lessons myself. (*Coyly touching* BRUCE'S *arm.*) Did you know that, Bruce ?

BRUCE (*moving away*). No, I did not.

(GWENNY *comes back from the kitchen, goes to the sideboard, takes the bowl of flowers, and puts it on the table.*)

ADA (*pointing to the wall over the fireplace*). Do you see that painting of a bunch of flowers ? Well, it's my work. It won a prize, it looked so natural. I could give you one or two hints on art, Bruce, if you like.

GWENNY. About what are you giving hints to him, Ada ? Iss it about pictures ? (*Seeing the pictures.*) Did you paint these, Bruce ? Give me a look, Susan. . . .

BRUCE (*above the table,* L. *of* GWENNY). They are what is called " Still Life." (*He puts his hat on the table.*)

GWENNY (*thoughtfully*). Still life . . . That iss a word that they use in painting, still life. . . .

MRS. HAGGETT (*turning from the desk*). What do you know about the words they use in painting ?

GWENNY. Oh, I know. . . . (*Pointing.*) Do you see this, Susan ? . . . He did not use his brush for it. No. He stick his thumb in the paint, and he go like this . . . (*indicating*) and like this——

BRUCE. That's right !

GWENNY (*to* BRUCE). Oh, I know. I know. . . .

ADA (*with her mother's dignity*). Don't take any notice of her, Mummy. Let her go into the kitchen and wash the dishes after Daddy's breakfast, and let Susan go and help her. And you go up to Daddy, and leave Bruce and me to hang the pictures up together.

(ADA *takes her picture and starts to rise.* BRUCE *turns his back on her.* GWENNY *takes the newspaper to the mantelpiece, then empties the ashtray on the medicine cabinet into the fireplace.* MRS. HAGGETT *starts for the stairs.* DR. HAGGETT *comes downstairs in his shirt-sleeves.*)

DR. HAGGETT. I go upstairs to shave, and there's no hot water. Morning, Bruce. How are you, my boy ?

MRS. HAGGETT. Susan, get a kettle of hot water for your father.

GWENNY (*as* SUSAN *rises*). Don't you worry yourself, Susan. I have no objections to fetching anything for your dad and for you.

MRS. HAGGETT (*crossing* R., *above the table*). If it were me, I suppose you'd tell me to shave in cold water ! (*She puts the table-napkin in the sideboard drawer.*)

(GWENNY *sweeps into the kitchen.*)

SUSAN (*quickly, picking up the pictures and crossing to* DR. HAGGETT). Oh, it's nothing, really, Daddy. Only Mummy and Gwenny having one of their usual tiffs. . . . Look what Bruce has painted for our dining-room !

DR. HAGGETT (*examining the pictures without much pleasure*). Hmmm . . . (*Looking at* ADA's *picture.*) Hmmmm . . .

BRUCE. If ye don't like this pair, Doctor Haggett, I got plenty more I painted doon in the shop.

SUSAN. How many, Bruce ?

Bruce. Oh, aboot a hundred.

Dr. Haggett. You must have taken a good deal of time off your regular painting to paint as many as that.

Bruce. I don't mind how much time I take off for painting pictures. I'm too gude to stay with paper-hanging.

Mrs. Haggett (*above chair* R. *of table*). You're not thinking of being an artist, I hope ?

Bruce. You bet your life I am, Mrs. Haggett ! And I'll be a gude one, too !

(Susan *puts the pictures down on the floor up* L., *leaning them against the upstage end of the desk.*)

Mrs. Haggett (*with wise decision*). No, Ada. No. I'm stopping here for a bit. (*Sitting on the chair* R. *of the table.*) I'd rather have a real painter in the family, rather than a picture painter.

Bruce (*above the table*). I was thinking of painting the garden gate for ye, Mrs. Haggett, but——

Mrs. Haggett (*sharply*). Free ?

Bruce. Free, gratis, and for nothing. But I've got a better idea now. I'll paint a portrait of the girls instead !

Susan. Oh, Bruce, will you really ?

Ada. Does Susan have to be in it ?

Bruce. She does indeed. Both of ye.

Dr. Haggett. You've come over very generous all of a sudden, haven't you, Bruce ?

Bruce. Well, Doctor, I started to think to meself one day, what good care ye took of my Aunty Allus, the time she died——

Dr. Haggett. Oh !

Bruce. And I started to think how ye never got any pay for that, and so——

Mrs. Haggett. If you're so very grateful, Bruce, perhaps you'll let us have the job you've just finished in the surgery, free ?

Bruce. Well, I'm not as grateful as all that.

Mrs. Haggett. Could you paint the girls and the garden gate ?

Bruce. I would, if ye would buy the paint for the gate.

Mrs. Haggett. Couldn't you use the portrait paint for the gate ?

Bruce. It's no the same kind, Mrs. Haggett.

Mrs. Haggett. Then I suppose we'll have to let the gate wait till next year's spring-cleaning.

Ada. What about the portrait, Mummy ?

Mrs. Haggett. Well, I haven't any particular use for it, but I've nothing particular against it.

Susan. How will you paint us, Bruce ?

(Bruce *studies the girls.*)

Dr. Haggett. Now that's a nice problem.

Bruce. Well, I don't know, really. I'll be forced to give a lot

of thought to the matter. Ada, you go over to that chair and sit
by Susan.

(ADA *goes to the armchair* L.C., *and sits.*)

DR. HAGGETT. Suppose Ada was listening to a sea-shell, and
Susan looking on, eh ?
BRUCE. No, Doctor, no. . . .
MRS. HAGGETT. How about them looking into the future, as it
were ?
BRUCE. I'll paint them just as they are !
ADA. Oh, not in this dress ! I've got a new one, and it'd look
quite lovely——
BRUCE. I like that dress. I like the colour. (*Thoroughly pro-
fessional.*) Your dress, and Susan's dress, and that old chair——
MRS. HAGGETT. That awful old chair that belonged to Doctor
Haggett's grandmother ! Have one of the nice new chintz covers
from the front bedroom——
BRUCE. No, the old things are the best. . . . Yes, I like it
fine. Just give me a bit of paper and a pencil. . . . (*He takes
them from the desk, then crosses back to above the table and studies the
girls.*)
ADA (*to* SUSAN). You sit down, and I'll stand behind.
SUSAN. Why ?
ADA (*pulling* SUSAN *into the chair*). I'm such a baby, Bruce
wouldn't want you towering over me, would you, Bruce ?

(*The girls change places,* ADA *arranging herself.*)

BRUCE. Och ! Any way will do. . . . That's fine. (*Sitting
on the chair above the table and beginning to sketch excitedly.*) Now,
you wait, Mrs. Haggett, and I'll give ye some slight idea of what
I can do. . . . (*To the girls.*) Don't move, now !

(*There is a pause.*)

MRS. HAGGETT. Mayn't Ada be holding a bunch of flowers in
her hand or something ?
ADA. It's Bruce's picture, Mummy. If he likes me as I am——
DR. HAGGETT (*leaning over* BRUCE'S *shoulder*). Look, Hannah !
You've got to admit the boy's quick with his pencil. You can see
which girl is which already.
MRS. HAGGETT (*looking*). Which *is* which ?
ADA. Does it look like me, Mummy ?
MRS. HAGGETT. No !
DR. HAGGETT. Give the boy time. You don't get likenesses as
quickly as all that. Do you, Bruce ?
MRS. HAGGETT. What do you know about it, Arthur ?
DR. HAGGETT. Well, I know that, anyway. Upon my soul,
Bruce, you're quite the artist. You'll be painting religious pictures
before you've finished !

BRUCE. Why releegious, Doctor ?

DR. HAGGETT. Haven't you seen all those big Biblical pictures in the Walker Art Gallery in Liverpool ? Marvellous ! Figures life-size, frames twenty feet long . . . marvellous ! " The Exodus from Egypt," " The Great Flood," " David and Goliath," " Potiphar's Wife "—fine Biblical pictures with a moral !

(DR. HAGGETT, *during this description, has come between* BRUCE *and the girls. He steps back quickly.*)

Where did you learn these tricks, Bruce ?

BRUCE (*still working*). Do you remember that painter here, called Chris Bean ?

DR. HAGGETT. Chris Bean ? He was a patient of mine. Funny, I had a telegram about him this morning.

MRS. HAGGETT. About Chris Bean ?

DR. HAGGETT. Yes. A chap who calls himself " an admirer of Christopher Bean." (*He fumbles for his coat pocket, and finds he is coatless.*)

MRS. HAGGETT. I don't know what he saw to admire in him.

(GWENNY *comes in* R. *with the kettle, and stops at the door.*)

BRUCE. Chris started me off on painting just after me father came here frae Edinburgh—about twelve I was then. He let me follow him wherever he went, and he let me sit by him and draw the same things he was drawing. He gave me lessons. The only lessons I got. I try to remember what he used to teach me, and——

(GWENNY *is fairly yearning towards the boy.*)

MRS. HAGGETT. I hope he didn't teach you to drink the same as he did.

GWENNY (*stiffening*). Well, if he—— (*As* MRS. HAGGETT *looks at her sharply.*) Here iss your kettle of hot water, Doctor Haggett. (*She gives the kettle to* DR. HAGGETT.)

DR. HAGGETT. What do I want with . . . Oh, yes, of course, I was shaving ! Well, I'd better get on with it, I suppose, and settle down to making my visits. Thank you, my dear.

(*He goes upstairs with the kettle.* GWENNY *and* MRS. HAGGETT *exchange a venomous look as* GWENNY *goes to the kitchen door.*)

GWENNY (*turning at the door*). Oh, Mrs. Haggett, I forgot to tell you. The real towny maid from Blackpool iss in the kitchen. I found her on the back doorstep when I went to fetch the kettle. I don't really hardly think she will be staying after what I told her about the place.

(*She goes back into the kitchen.*)

MRS. HAGGETT (*rising and going towards the kitchen*). If Gwenny's gone and poisoned that new maid's mind—— !

ADA. Excuse me a minute, Bruce, this is important. . . . Oh, Mummy! Do you think——

(*She follows her mother into the kitchen.*)

SUSAN (*crossing to* BRUCE). Will you let me see, Bruce?

BRUCE (*rising and stepping towards her*). If ye want to. It's only the rough beginning, of course.

SUSAN. It looks to me as if it isn't quite fair to Ada.

BRUCE. Well, so long as it's fair to you . . .

SUSAN. Oh, no, Bruce! (*Taking a step away.*) You must be fair to Ada, or Mummy'll be on top of you like a ton of bricks.

BRUCE. I paint pictures to suit meself, and not to suit your mother. I don't care two hoots for yer mother, or for Ada neether. . . . You know fine why I'm painting this picture.

SUSAN (*drawing back*). You said you wanted to give Mother a present.

BRUCE. All I want is an excuse to see you every day.

SUSAN. Oh, Bruce, you've known me too long to begin talking such nonsense!

BRUCE. And you've known me long enough to know what I think aboot you.

SUSAN. I don't think you'd better say any more, Bruce.

BRUCE. All right; you say ye'll marry me, and I won't say any more.

SUSAN. Bruce!

BRUCE. What d'ye mean, Bruce?

SUSAN. But I just wouldn't be the right wife for you. Not if you're going to be an artist, anyway.

BRUCE. Why wouldn't ye be the right wife for me? I'm a hard worker, I'm going to be a gude artist, and after all, I am Scotch.

SUSAN. Yes, but I don't even know that I like art . . . much.

BRUCE. I'll teach ye to like it.

SUSAN. You haven't even told me you love me.

BRUCE. Do I have to tell ye that?

SUSAN. Well, I think you ought to.

BRUCE. Ye can't take my word for it?

SUSAN. All right, Bruce. There's one thing, though. We'd have to wait for Ada to get married first.

BRUCE. Huh!

SUSAN. We wouldn't have a minute's peace if we didn't do that.

BRUCE (*putting the drawing on the table and turning to her*). I'm thinking I'd better gie ye a kiss.

SUSAN. Why?

BRUCE. Well, it's you I'm marrying, not Ada, and I'm busy right up to my neck, and I've got no time to waste! Besides, I have an idea that being kissed will stop your nonsense.

SUSAN. Well, you never know, perhaps it will.

BRUCE. You're not afraid?

SUSAN. No!

BRUCE. All right. I'll do it, then.

(*He takes her stiffly in his arms and kisses her with little passion. The kitchen door opens, and ADA appears.*)

ADA. Well, Bruce, here I am back—— (*She sees them and gasps—calling.*) Daddy! Mummy! Come here, quick!

(SUSAN *breaks away from* BRUCE, *to* L. DR. HAGGETT *appears on the stairs, still in his shirt-sleeves.*)

DR. HAGGETT. What's the matter?

BRUCE. It's Ada that's meddling aboot in other people's affairs.

ADA. Don't you dare speak to me!

(MRS. HAGGETT *comes in from the kitchen.*)

MRS. HAGGETT. Ada, you know how busy I am. What do you want?

ADA (*beside herself*). I don't care how busy you are! There are things going on here that want seeing to, and badly, too!

DR. HAGGETT (*coming into the room*). What's come over this house this morning? (*He is* C.)

ADA. I was in the kitchen, Daddy, with Mummy and the new servant, and I came in here, and caught him and her—Susan . . .

BRUCE (*stepping forward, undismayed*). Ye don't have to tell them what I was doing, Ada. I'd sooner show them. (*He takes the terrified* SUSAN *in his arms and kisses her again, this time with real passion.*)

(*A gasp from* MRS. HAGGETT.)

DR. HAGGETT. God bless my soul!

MRS. HAGGETT (*crossing to* C., *below the table—furious*). You take your rubbish out of this respectable God-fearing house, young man!

BRUCE. All right. I don't mind. Are ye coming with me, Susan? Susan and me are going to get married.

ADA (*shrilly*). Mummy, if you let Susan get married before I do . . .!

(DR. HAGGETT *tries to stop* ADA. *The positions are:* ADA *below* L. *of table,* DR. HAGGETT L. *of* ADA, MRS. HAGGETT C., BRUCE L.C., *and* SUSAN *below and just* L. *of* BRUCE.)

MRS. HAGGETT. Susan is not going to marry Bruce McRae, or anybody remotely resembling him. (*Facing* BRUCE.) My daughter is far too good to waste on a starving, ragamuffin artist!

BRUCE (*with great dignity*). Mrs. Haggett, I really cannot believe that in those words ye are speaking of me, Mrs. Haggett, really I can't. I am the best bet for marriage in Childer Barnston, and all the country round from Chester on one side to Yorrk on the other. I am going far, Mrs. Haggett ; and your daughter Susan is coming with me. I think she's old enough to know her own mind. Eh, Susan ?

SUSAN. Please go along now, Bruce. Talking like this won't do any good. Really, it won't. . . .

BRUCE. I won't go unless you come with me.

MRS. HAGGETT (*turning to* DR. HAGGETT). Arthur, if that creature isn't out of the house by the time I count ten, I'm going to call on you to throw him out !

(DR. HAGGETT *tries to restrain* MRS. HAGGETT.)

SUSAN. There'll be no need to throw Bruce out, Daddy. Please go, Bruce. I'll see you later.

(MRS. HAGGETT *goes to the table.*)

BRUCE (*as steadily as ever*). When ?

SUSAN. I'll send you a message.

DR. HAGGETT. You go, Bruce, there's a good chap. And let things simmer down, eh ?

BRUCE. All right, Doctor. Just give me back my drawing. . . .

(DR. HAGGETT *crosses to* SUSAN. MRS. HAGGETT *picks up the drawing from the table, crumples it up and throws it into the fireplace. There is a general gasp.*)

MRS. HAGGETT. There'll be no more painting portraits in this house !

BRUCE (*picking up his hat from the table and suddenly going*). I'll go, to keep the peace for Susan's sake. (*He opens the front door, then turns.*) But she ought to come with me. Because we are going to get married. I'll go now. But I'll show ye yet ! And as for you, Mrs. Doctor Arthur Haggett, ye're what they call in London a Philistine.

(*He goes out, slamming the door.* SUSAN *bursts into tears.*)

MRS. HAGGETT. Well, Philistine or not, I think I've nipped that little romance in the bud. Huh, Philistine !

(SUSAN *sits in the chair at the desk.*)

DR. HAGGETT (*perplexed*). Well, it's out of the Bible, Hannah.

MRS. HAGGETT. I don't care what it's out of, Arthur ; he didn't mean it as a compliment.

DR. HAGGETT. Now you two had better clear out, and leave me and Susan to have a little talk.

MRS. HAGGETT. I said this was going to be an upsetting morning, but I'd no idea how upsetting. . . .

ADA. If you let Susan——

MRS. HAGGETT. Oh, go into the kitchen——

(*She pushes* ADA *before her into the kitchen.*)

DR. HAGGETT (*comforting* SUSAN). Now, now, my dear. Now, now, my own little Susan . . . that's better, eh ?

SUSAN. He loves me, Daddy, and I love him !

DR. HAGGETT. Well, that's a pity, of course. If he weren't so dead set on being an artist——

SUSAN. What's wrong with artists ?

DR. HAGGETT. Nothing, except the cost of food and lodging.

(TALLANT *passes by the window.*)

SUSAN. Not if he is a good artist ! And he will be a good artist !

DR. HAGGETT. He's swollen-headed enough to be. But the best of them are very poor providers, from all I hear ; and in these days, of course——

SUSAN (*passionately*). These days ! That's all you talk about, these days ! If it weren't for these days, you and Mummy wouldn't have a thing against Bruce, and Mummy and Ada could go to the Isle of Man.

(*The front-door bell rings.*)

DR. HAGGETT. And I could get a little peace.

(SUSAN *rises.*)

Here we are talking our heads off, and me with all my visits still to make. (*Starting upstairs.*) Come upstairs, my dear, and wash your face, and I'll put my coat on. I'll have a chat with Bruce, and I'll see what can be done. . . .

(*To* GWENNY, *who comes in from the kitchen very concerned.*)

If that's a patient, Gwenny, show him in here and keep the others out. I'll be down in two shakes of a lamb's tail.

(*He goes upstairs with* SUSAN. GWENNY *opens the front door to admit* TALLANT, *a smooth, youngish and well-dressed Londoner, with a minor public-school education. He is wearing a well-cut tweed coat and waistcoat, and smart grey flannel trousers.*)

GWENNY. Will you step in here, plees ? The Doctor will be down in two shakes of a lamb's tail.

(*She closes the front door. They come into the room.*)

TALLANT. Thank you, I'll wait, then.

GWENNY. You can have a chair if you like. There wass some of last year's magazines in the surgery ; but they wass lost in the moving, you see, on account of the surgery being painted : but the Doctor will not keep you long, he will not really. (*She crosses to the door* R.)

(TALLANT *looks quickly round the room, goes to* ADA'S *picture up* R.C.,

looks at it expectantly, and turns away disappointed. He catches
GWENNY'S *eye and smiles.*)

TALLANT (*slowly, casually*). Thank you. . . . You must be
Gwenny.

GWENNY (*after a pause—surprised*). I never see you before, that
I can remember.

(TALLANT *puts his turned-down soft felt hat on the cabinet up* R.C.)

TALLANT. No, this is the first time we've ever met.

GWENNY. How does it come to pass that you walk in here, then,
and call me by my Christian name, ass bold ass brass?

TALLANT. Ever heard of mind-readers?

GWENNY. Goodness me, you are not one of them heathens, are
you?

TALLANT. Only in a small way.

GWENNY. Whatever you are, you are as cheeky as they make
them. You don't have to be so downy just because you come
from London.

(*She goes into the kitchen.* DR. HAGGETT *comes downstairs.*)

DR. HAGGETT. Good morning. (*He comes into the room.*)

TALLANT. Am I addressing Doctor Haggett?

DR. HAGGETT. You are.

(*They shake hands.*)

TALLANT (*over-elaborate*). I'm very glad to have met you, Doctor
Haggett.

DR. HAGGETT (*pointing to the chair down* L.). Sit down, won't
you? . . . I'm sorry, but my surgery is out of action. (*He sits
at the desk.*)

TALLANT. Don't apologize, Doctor. I've called because I feel——

DR. HAGGETT. A little bilious? Yes, you look it.

(TALLANT *interrupts.*)

You can't fool me where a sluggish liver is concerned. I've been a
martyr to it all my life.

TALLANT I daresay you're right, Doctor, but . . .

DR. HAGGETT. Sit down and put your tongue out.

(TALLANT *goes to the armchair* L.C.)

Headache? Nausea? Bowels all right?

TALLANT. You don't understand, Doctor. I'm as fit as a
fiddle. (*He pulls the armchair to downstage* L.C.)

DR. HAGGETT. Well, if you're as fit as a fiddle, what do you
want me for?

TALLANT. I was just coming to that. (*He sits in the armchair.*)

DR. HAGGETT (*rising, impatiently*). Now, I may as well tell you at the outset that I don't want any insurance.

TALLANT. I'm not here to sell insurance.

(DR. HAGGETT *grunts.*)

I'm not here to sell anything. I'm here solely for the pleasure of making your acquaintance !

DR. HAGGETT (*rather ironically*). That's very nice of you !

TALLANT (*in a softer tone*). Oh, yes, I am ! I happened to be motoring through your lovely Marvin dales, enjoying the beauty of the spring foliage——

(DR. HAGGETT *shows signs of impatience and sits down again.*)

And as I came to the village of Childer Barnston, I realized I'd stumbled on an opportunity to perform a duty I've postponed too long.

DR. HAGGETT. And what duty is that ?

TALLANT. The payment of a sacred debt I owe you, Doctor.

DR. HAGGETT (*making a quick turn to* TALLANT). And what debt do you owe me, in Heaven's name ?

TALLANT. A matter of ten years ago, you had a patient, a man whom I called—and still call—my dearest friend.

DR. HAGGETT. You don't say so !

TALLANT. A West Country lad, Doctor, an orphan who lived for some time in Childer Barnston. I am referring to Christopher Bean.

DR. HAGGETT (*enlightened*). Oh, it's you, is it ?

TALLANT (*startled*). I beg your pardon ?

DR. HAGGETT (*laughing*). And I took you for a patient ; can you beat that ! But I wasn't expecting you for some hours yet.

TALLANT (*on his guard*). You were expecting *me* ?

DR. HAGGETT. Well, I got your telegram, Mr. . . . (*Fumbling in his pocket.*) Let me see now, what was the name ?

TALLANT (*rising—quickly*). Is that the telegram ? (*He snatches it.*) May I see it ? . . . They so often mix them up. . . .

DR. HAGGETT. That looks plain enough.

TALLANT (*reading it—quickly*). Oh, yes. Quite. I forgot I'd said " twelve noon." (*Returning it.*) It took me less time to get here than I thought. (*Sitting again.*) I hurried. (*Smiling, his affability restored.*) I was afraid I might miss you. And I was so eager, you see, so very eager . . .

DR. HAGGETT (*looking at the telegram*). You say here that you're an admirer of Chris Bean.

TALLANT. That's putting it very mildly, Doctor Haggett.

DR. HAGGETT. I'm just wondering if your Chris Bean and mine are the same.

TALLANT. Oh, I'm certain . . .

DR. HAGGETT. I'm not so sure. As my wife said when this telegram arrived—" I can't see what he finds to admire about Chris Bean ! "—those were her very words. My wife leans a little towards the strait-laced, if you follow me, sir.

TALLANT. Quite, quite.

DR. HAGGETT. Not that Chris wasn't a very likeable young fellow. I was fond of him.

TALLANT. Of course you were.

DR. HAGGETT. I just want to make sure. . . . Did the chap you're thinking of fancy himself as a bit of a painter ?

TALLANT (surprised). Well, you might put it like that.

DR. HAGGETT. It's the same fellow, then. (He puts the telegram on the desk.)

TALLANT. Yes, poor chap.

DR. HAGGETT (confidentially). Oh, we used to humour him about his pictures. You've got to humour a man who's as far gone in health as poor Chris was.

TALLANT. I know you did everything you could for him.

DR. HAGGETT. Well, I hope I did my duty. But in a case like that, you know . . . This part of the British Isles is no climate for tuberculosis. If he had the wherewithal to get himself down to Cornwall or the South of France, he might have stood a chance ; if he'd kept off the drink. But as it was, there wasn't much I could do.

TALLANT. We're all mortal, Doctor.

DR. HAGGETT. Yes, you're right there.

TALLANT. It delights me that you remember him with so much affection.

DR. HAGGETT. Oh, we haven't forgotten him, you know ; we were talking about him only a few minutes ago. My wife took quite a fancy to him, as it were. I suppose he appealed to her, in a way, because we haven't any boys in the family. And with him coming to live here, and a sick man too, and an orphan into the bargain . . . She took him so much to her heart, she gave him a studio.

TALLANT. Did she really ?

DR. HAGGETT. Yes, the old cowshed at the bottom of the back garden. (Laughing reminiscently.) They were appalling, though, those pictures. If the boy had studied art at the Exfield Grammar School——

TALLANT (quickly). Yes, I daresay you're right. . . . (Seriously.) Recently, though, Doctor—only the other day, in fact—as I was going through an old desk of mine, I came across some letters Chris wrote me while he was living here. And in the last of them—it's disgraceful of me to have neglected it all these years—he spoke of your kindness to him, and his gratitude, and asked if I couldn't help him to pay back what he owed you.

DR. HAGGETT (pleased). Well, if that isn't like old Chris ! Never a penny to his name; it was borrow, borrow, borrow, morning, noon and night. . . . He didn't even have a hat of his own!

TALLANT. Let me see . . . the sum came to . . .

DR. HAGGETT (*quite sincerely*). Oh, I don't remember now.

TALLANT (*firmly*). Exactly twenty pounds.

DR. HAGGETT. I daresay it was, yes. . . . What probably happened was that I told him that if ever he had twenty pounds he thought he could spare——

TALLANT. Allow me, Doctor. (*He rises, and hands out to* DR. HAGGETT *four five-pound notes.*) A little late, but paid in full.

DR. HAGGETT (*amazed*). Good Lord!

TALLANT. And all my apologies for keeping you waiting.

DR. HAGGETT (*rising*). My dear sir. (*He takes the money.*)

TALLANT. Well, the debt's paid at last. I shall go back to London a happier man.

DR. HAGGETT (*completely flabbergasted*). I'll give you a receipt.

TALLANT (*protesting*). Oh, Doctor, please——

DR. HAGGETT. Would you allow me, sir, to shake you by the hand?

TALLANT. I should be honoured.

(*They shake hands.*)

DR. HAGGETT. Just a minute. (*Calling.*) Hannah! Ada! (*He crosses to the door* R.) I want you to meet my family, Mr. . . . Mr. . . . Davenport.

TALLANT. I'm sorry, I left my visiting-cards in my Chester hotel.

DR. HAGGETT. I don't need any visiting-card from you! (*Touching his heart.*) Your name is engraved here.

(MRS. HAGGETT *and* ADA *come in* R.   MRS. HAGGETT *crosses to* TALLANT.)

(*Introducing.*) My wife . . . My daughter Ada . . . (*He looks upstairs.*) My younger daughter is upstairs resting—she is not feeling very well. (*To* MRS. HAGGETT *and* ADA.) I called you two in here to present you to an honest man.

TALLANT. Don't be alarmed, please, ladies.

(*The positions are:* ADA *below the table, then, from* R *to* L., DR. HAGGETT, MRS. HAGGETT, TALLANT.)

DR. HAGGETT. Mr. Davenport here, who sent me that telegram from London, is a friend of our old friend Chris Bean—the very same boy we were discussing this morning, Hannah. And now, ten years after Chris passed away, as it were, this loyal friend, this more than honest man, has called to pay me the little debt that Chris owed me. Twenty pounds! Things like that don't happen every day.

MRS. HAGGETT (*profoundly impressed*). They certainly don't!

DR. HAGGETT. Let this be an example and an inspiration to you both !

ADA. Yes, Daddy.

MRS. HAGGETT. It will, Arthur, it will. (*To* TALLANT, *crossing to the armchair.*) Won't you sit down and rest yourself ?

(TALLANT *sits in the armchair* L.C. MRS. HAGGETT *crosses and sits* L. *of the table.*)

DR. HAGGETT (*crossing to the desk*). And whatever you do, you two, you must neither of you ever forget the name of . . . (*He hesitates.*)

TALLANT. Davenport.

DR. HAGGETT (*sitting at the desk*). Davenport ! It was just on the tip of my tongue.

(ADA *sits on the chair below the table.*,

TALLANT. Really, Doctor, you cover me with confusion. I see nothing extraordinary in what I've done.

DR. HAGGETT. You try your hand at collecting doctors' bills these days, and you'll soon see ! (*He picks up his cash-book, makes an entry in it, and mutters gleefully,* "Twenty pounds.")

TALLANT. And I told you how much my friend meant to me !

(*There is a pause. They look solemn.*)

(*The merest afterthought.*) I'm just wondering if he didn't leave any of his pictures to remember him by. Of course, you've told me what you thought of them.

(MRS. HAGGETT *looks down.*)

And Chris wrote how even the village lads laughed at him when they watched him painting. . . .

DR. HAGGETT. It's rather an unkind thing to say, but I'm afraid they did.

MRS. HAGGETT. We never let him see *us* laughing.

TALLANT (*after a pause, to* MRS. HAGGETT). They'd have a special sentimental value for me, you can understand.

DR. HAGGETT. Well, there's nothing to be ashamed of in that.

TALLANT (*to* DR. HAGGETT). Then if you have any pictures, do you think I might take them away with me ? (*More specific.*) His letters mention six or seven he left here.

DR. HAGGETT. Oh, there were at least that, yes.

(TALLANT *gives him a look.*)

MRS. HAGGETT. Arthur, I believe there's one still outside in the chicken-house !

TALLANT (*barely suppressing horror*). The chicken-house !

DR. HAGGETT. Hannah, you're right ! There is ! (*Apologetic-*

ally, to TALLANT.) But I hate to think of the condition it must be in.

TALLANT (*the least pause, then quickly*). I'd like to have it, Doctor. It doesn't matter what condition it's in, I'd like to have it. It is a souvenir, you know.

MRS. HAGGETT (*rising*). Come with me, Ada. We'll see if we can get it for Mr. Davenport.

(*She goes out* C., *and to* R. *down the passage, followed by* ADA.)

DR. HAGGETT. Yes, I remember now. There was a leak in the roof of the chicken-house ; I was looking round for something water-tight, and I found that picture. It was good thick oil paint, you know, and there was no reason for attaching any value to it, as it were.

TALLANT (*weakly*). No.

DR. HAGGETT (*rising and crossing to* C.). Wait ! . . . (*Calling.*) Gwenny ! . . . (*To* TALLANT.) Another idea has just occurred to me.

(GWENNY *enters and crosses above the table to* R.C.)

Gwenny, run up to the attic, and look in the corner, just under the little window that'll never open. . . . I seem to remember we used one of those pictures of Chris Bean's to stop a leak there as well.

GWENNY (*starting guiltily, and gulping*). What iss it you want with the picture, Doctor Haggett ?

DR. HAGGETT. Mr. Davenport here wants to take it home with him.

GWENNY. Mistar Davenport wants to take it home ?

(TALLANT *looks at* GWENNY.)

DR. HAGGETT. Mr. Davenport was Chris Bean's oldest friend.

GWENNY. Mistar Davenport was ?

DR. HAGGETT. Yes. (*Crossing to the desk.*) Now go and see if you can get that picture off without tearing it. And then bring it down here.

GWENNY. For Mistar Davenport ?

DR. HAGGETT. Exactly.

GWENNY. Yes, Doctor Haggett.

(*She goes upstairs.* DR. HAGGETT *sits at the desk.*)

TALLANT. I'm sorry to cause your household so much trouble.

DR. HAGGETT. My dear fellow, a man like you isn't any trouble at all. I only hope we can find what you're looking for.

(MRS. HAGGETT *and* ADA *return.*)

ADA (*coming to above the table*). Well, here it is.

MRS. HAGGETT (*coming down* C.). Here we are. (*Holding out a filthy square of canvas.*) It's a bit dirty, but you know what chickens are.

DR. HAGGETT (*rising*). Well, you let Gwenny get at it with a bit of carbolic soap and a scrubbing-brush——

TALLANT (*rising—hastily*). No, no, no! That won't be necessary! (*He snatches the picture.*)

MRS. HAGGETT (C.). I assure you it wouldn't be any trouble.

TALLANT (R.C.). Oh, no, please! I'd be afraid . . . I mean I'd rather clean it up myself.

MRS. HAGGETT. But you can't carry it off in the nasty condition it's in now!

DR. HAGGETT. Impossible!

TALLANT. Don't you see, Doctor, what it will mean to me to bring this picture back to life? It will seem almost as if Chris himself . . .

(*There is a pause in honour of his emotion.*)

MRS. HAGGETT. Oh, yes. (*To* DR. HAGGETT.) Arthur, you didn't think of Ada's picture over there. (*She points to the picture over the mantelpiece.*)

DR. HAGGETT. But Mr. Davenport doesn't want Ada's pictures!

ADA (*above the table*). Of course he doesn't want any pictures painted by little me! But Mummy means I turned over one of Chris Bean's pictures, and painted my bunch of flowers on the back. (*She moves to* R. *of the table.*)

(TALLANT *looks at the picture.*)

DR. HAGGETT. Well, I never knew that. (*He goes to the mantelpiece and takes the picture down.*) Now isn't that a pity, Mr. Davenport? There's another we might have given you if Ada hadn't gone daubing it.

(TALLANT *puts the canvas on the chair* L. *of the table.*)

I'm not blaming you, Ada, but——

TALLANT (L. *of the table, taking the picture from* DR. HAGGETT, *who is above the table*). Did you paint this, Miss Haggett?

(MRS. HAGGETT *is down* L.)

ADA (*archly*). If you *can* call it painting . . . well, I did.

TALLANT. This lovely, living thing!

ADA. Oh, Mr. Davenport! I did take a few lessons once, but . . .

TALLANT. You painted this little masterpiece on a few lessons?

ADA (*happily*). It isn't a masterpiece, Mr. Davenport! At least, I'd never call it that!

TALLANT. My dear Miss Haggett, don't underrate your gifts! The exquisite texture of those buttercups is not to be expressed in words.

ADA (*excited*). Mummy! Did you hear what Mr. Davenport said?

TALLANT. Of course, I didn't mean that you won't do better things in the future, or that you won't go further. But here, already, I, the connoisseur, sense the spark of genius!

DR. HAGGETT (*up R.C.*). Genius!

TALLANT. I do, really! (*He looks at the Christopher Bean portrait on the other side.*)

(ADA *is down* R.)

MRS. HAGGETT. Now, Mr. Davenport, don't you go turning our little Ada into an artist!

(DR. HAGGETT *comes down to the chair* L. *of the table.*)

TALLANT (*crossing to* MRS. HAGGETT). Of course, I know you won't want to part with it, but if you'll let me buy it. . . .

MRS. HAGGETT (L.C., *quickly*). What is it worth?

TALLANT (C., *holding it*). That's hard to say. Her name isn't known yet, but I should think the better London dealers . . .

DR. HAGGETT. I know! Christie's, perhaps.

TALLANT. Yes, perhaps. . . . Now they could sell a thing like this for . . . let me see . . . twelve guineas? Not that it isn't worth much more!

ADA. Twelve guineas!

TALLANT (*quickly*). Well, say ten.

ADA. But I could do one like that every day!

TALLANT. Then don't hesitate, Miss Haggett. Your fortune's made. (*He crosses to the table and lays the picture face upwards on it.*)

DR. HAGGETT (*oddly dubious, crossing to* L.C.). Now I come to think of it, it strikes me as a little bit odd, your coming here and paying Chris Bean's debt, and offering my little girl ten guineas——

MRS. HAGGETT. Twelve.

DR. HAGGETT. He said ten.

MRS. HAGGETT. He said twelve first, and twelve is Ada's price.

TALLANT. I'll pay twelve, naturally, if you'll sell it. (*Producing his wallet and extracting more notes.*) And you may be sure that orders for more will follow.

DR. HAGGETT. I don't know that Ada ought to take this money, Hannah.

ADA. But, Daddy, a girl like me can find plenty of ways of spending twelve guineas, even if we don't go to the Isle of Man!

TALLANT. There's twelve . . . and a ten-shilling note . . . and two shillings. . . . There!

ADA (*taking the money*). Thank you, Mr. Davenport.

TALLANT. Thank *you*, Miss Haggett, for the very great pleasure of discovering a new artist.

ADA. Oh, Mr. Davenport!

DR. HAGGETT (*somewhat ashamed*). She gets it all from me, I'm afraid. Even though I am a doctor, I've always had a weakness for art.

ADA. And you've got Chris Bean's picture on the other side of mine.

TALLANT (*picking up the picture—with a false laugh*). By Jove, so I have! (*Turning the picture over.*) Do you know, in my enthusiasm for your work, I'd quite forgotten . . . (*We see that he is struck by its beauty.*)

(*There is a pause.*)

DR. HAGGETT (*looking at it*). And what do you think he was getting at, that time ?

ADA. Isn't it meant to be the old stone bridge where the Grassmere road goes past Orchard Farm ?

MRS. HAGGETT (*moving to him*). Arthur, why don't you try looking at it the right side up ? (*She pulls DR. HAGGETT by the right arm.*)

DR. HAGGETT. Upon my word, it looks the same to me either way . . .

(TALLANT *looks at* DR. HAGGETT.)

(*Remembering, to* TALLANT.) I beg your pardon, Mr. Davenport, I'm sure—I shouldn't have said that, about the deceased . . . (*As they all look solemn.*) Especially feeling about him as you do.

(MRS. HAGGETT *sits in the chair at the desk.* GWENNY *comes downstairs and eyes* TALLANT *with suspicion.*)

GWENNY (*up* C.). I could not find anything in the attic, Doctor. There iss no picture there, no pictures whatever.

(TALLANT *drops the picture to his side.*)

DR. HAGGETT. But I know I put——
MRS. HAGGETT. Perhaps the mice have been at it.

(TALLANT *picks up the canvas from the chair* L. *of the table.*)

DR. HAGGETT. But, my dear girl, I put it there with my own hands, just under the little window with the cobwebs all over it——
GWENNY (*very steadily, standing above the armchair* L.C.). There iss nothing there now only some empty jam-jars that Mrs. Haggett iss saving up.

DR. HAGGETT. But I tell you I'm positive !

GWENNY (*not to be shaken*). I have been over every bit of that attic, every jobbin of it. I did not find nothing there, only the old iron bedstead that use to be in the best bedroom till you got the second-hand wooden one from——

MRS. HAGGETT. That'll do, Gwenny Thomas, in front of strangers.

GWENNY. There is a box with your mother's old Worcestershire cups and saucers in it, and the other box——

DR. HAGGETT. Well, I'm damned ! I could have sworn——

Mrs. Haggett. You are swearing, Arthur, and I don't like it.

Dr. Haggett. Well, that's a great pity, Mr. Davenport.

(Gwenny *crosses above the desk.*)

I'd have liked to show you how much I appreciate all you've done, but there we are. Nobody can do better than his best, can he, eh ?

Tallant. I'm more than satisfied with what I've got, Doctor Haggett. But I repeat I'm only sorry to have caused you so much trouble.

Dr. Haggett. Oh, my dear fellow, no trouble at all.

Tallant (*bowing as they brush aside his apologies with low exclamations*). Mrs. Haggett. Miss Haggett. (*He goes to the cabinet for his hat.*)

Dr. Haggett (L. *of* c. *opening, escorting him into the passage*). Mr. Davenport, your visit this morning is going to stand out in my mind as one of the happiest memories of my medical career.

Tallant (R. *of* c. *opening, turning suddenly at the door*). Doctor Haggett, you and I are going to know each other very much better. And it occurs to me that we might go into business together . . . business which might be highly profitable to both of us.

Dr. Haggett. But I haven't got any capital.

Tallant. It will require nothing more of you than . . . (*laughing*) friendly co-operation.

Dr. Haggett (*smiling*). Oh, I've got plenty of that !

Tallant. Then we're rich men, Doctor Haggett.

(*They shake hands. He goes out of the front door and is seen passing the window.*)

Mrs. Haggett (*after a pause, rising*). Well ! At this rate we may get to the Isle of Man after all ! (*She crosses to above the table.*)

Dr. Haggett (*coming back, and going to his desk*). Well, after this morning, I'm not so sure you won't. (*He sits.*) I wish I knew what the business is he's got in his mind. . . .

Ada. I don't care what it is, so long as it makes us rich.

(Gwenny *at the window has watched* Tallant *down the road.*)

Dr. Haggett (*sentimentally and sternly*). Ada, that's no way for any daughter of mine to talk. If there's one thing in this world I can't abide, it's greed for money.

Ada. Let's get down to the grocer's, Mummy, before Daddy gets started.

Mrs. Haggett. Yes, Ada, come upstairs and put your hat on. (*As they both go upstairs.*) If anything ever did happen to make us rich, I wouldn't worry very much what it was.

(Ada *puts her hand on the banisters.*)

Don't touch that paint, Ada.

(*They disappear.*)

B

(DR. HAGGETT *sits at his desk, smiling dreamily. Suddenly he rouses himself, looks at his watch, is shocked by the late hour, and prepares for his calls.*)

DR. HAGGETT (*rising and moving to* c.). Have you seen my visiting-list, Gwenny ?

GWENNY (*taking it out of the top drawer of the desk*). Here it iss, Doctor Haggett. (*She gives it to him.*)

DR. HAGGETT (L.C., *looking at it*). I'll call at Henry Briggs's farm first. The rest are in the village. (*He picks up his bag.*)

GWENNY. I have got them all written down, Doctor.

DR. HAGGETT. Then you know where to get hold of me if I'm wanted.

(*There is a pause. He slips back into his reveries, then recalls himself.*)

(*Laughing apologetically.*) There I go, day-dreaming again ! That fellow Davenport's taken my doctoring clean out of my head.

GWENNY. If I wass you, Doctor, I would keep my eye on him, careful.

DR. HAGGETT (*going out to the hall for his hat and coat*). Why would you keep your eye on him, Gwenny ?

GWENNY. Well, in my idear of things, Doctor Haggett, it iss a good idear to watch people pretty close when they know ass much ass he knows.

(DR. HAGGETT *is in the* c. *opening, putting on his coat.*)

DR. HAGGETT (*testily*). You know, Gwenny, I don't think Mrs. Haggett's very far wrong about the way you interfere in other people's business. Didn't I get a wire from him this morning about Chris Bean ?

(*She says nothing.* DR. HAGGETT *picks up his bag which he has deposited for a moment on the table just off* L., *opens the front door and leaves the house. He passes the window.* GWENNY *stands still. She looks at the telegram, picks it up, but hastily puts it down again on the desk as* MRS. HAGGETT *and* ADA *come chattering downstairs, ready to go out.*)

MRS. HAGGETT (*on the stairs*). Are you ready, Ada ?

(ADA *appears behind her on the stairs.*)

On second thoughts, Ada dear, I don't think I'll take back that artificial silk just yet.

(GWENNY *has gone to the armchair* L.C., *and moves it up again to its original position.*)

ADA. Oh, I wouldn't, Mummy, really ! You heard Daddy say we might get to the Isle of Man after all. We might even get as far as Gleneagles—I've always wanted to go there for my holidays. . . .

(*They go out by the front door.* GWENNY *watches them pass the window, and again picks up the telegram. She reads it through, pronouncing every word inaudibly to herself. A clock strikes ten.* SUSAN *comes downstairs, wiping her eyes.* GWENNY *holds the telegram out of her sight.* SUSAN *picks up* BRUCE'S *drawing from the fireplace and brings it to the table, where she smoothes it out lovingly.*)

GWENNY (*crossing below the armchair*). Susan!

SUSAN (*by the chair* R. *of the table*). Oh, Gwenny, I never thought anybody could feel as miserable as I do now!

GWENNY. Oh, ynghariadi, people can be miserable sometimes something terrible. (*She comes to the chair* L. *of the table.*)

SUSAN (*sitting on the chair* R. *of the table*). But look at poor Bruce's drawing, all crumpled up! Gwenny, it's ruined!

GWENNY. He will make another one.

(SUSAN *looks at her.*)

(L. *of the table.*) Artists always do.

SUSAN. Gwenny, *you* haven't got anything against artists, have you?

GWENNY. Me? (*She moves to the chair below the table.*) Oh, no—not me! (*She smiles to herself.*)

CURTAIN.

ACT II

The SCENE *is the same. It is a little later, about noon.*
Bright sunshine still pours into the room through the windows.
The furniture is arranged exactly as before, only a few of the luncheon
things are placed ready on the sideboard. The double-doors up C.
are open ; the kitchen door down R. *is shut.*
(See Furniture and Property Plot.)

The CURTAIN *rises on an empty stage. Almost immediately* TALLANT
is seen passing the window, then the front-door bell rings. GWENNY
enters down R. *and moves up above the table to the hall to answer the*
door. She admits TALLANT, *but stands with her hand on the knob*
of the open door, eyeing him suspiciously.

GWENNY. The Doctor is still out making his calls.

TALLANT (*coming into the hall, to* R. *of her*). It was you I came
back to see, Gwenny.

GWENNY (*surprised*). Me ? (*She eyes him more narrowly than*
ever as she closes the door.)

(TALLANT *enters the room and puts his hat on the medical cabinet.*)

TALLANT. If you can spare a moment, I'd like to talk to you.

(GWENNY *follows to* L. *of him.*)

GWENNY (*challengingly*). And whatever have you in your head
to say to me ?

(*After a pause* TALLANT *steps to her and puts his left hand on her*
shoulder.)

TALLANT. " Thank you."

GWENNY. And what in the world are you thanking me for ?

TALLANT. For being kind once, to a friend of mine. For giving
him things that other women denied him. You gave him all the
good things that have no name. All the warm, tender things he so
badly needed.

(*She draws back a step. He drops his hand.*)

GWENNY (*really frightened*). What do you know about me ?

TALLANT (*simply*). Only what he told me. Except for you, I
was the best friend he ever had.

GWENNY (*with swift, low intensity*). I never heard him speak of
36

no Davenport ! He used to talk a lot about his friend James Brown. But I never heard of you !

TALLANT. I am James Brown.

GWENNY (*scornfully*). Well, if you are James Brown, what for are you calling yourself Davenport ?

TALLANT (*elaborately*). Davenport's my professional name. I needed a name people would remember, and Maxwell Davenport——

GWENNY (*still scornfully*). Besides, if you are James Brown, that would not be the reason why you change your name.

TALLANT. Oh, why ?

GWENNY. Well, I happen to know that James Brown got into a bit of trouble. He owed a lot of money, and he could not pay it back. So he left the place he wass living in, full speed. Well, anyway, that is how Chris told me it wass.

TALLANT. You remember all that, do you ?

GWENNY. I have not forgot one thing that Chris told me, not one thing. . . . Besides, you don't look ass I expect James Brown to look, neither !

TALLANT (*flattering*). You look exactly as I expected you to look, Gwenny, only younger and prettier. And I knew your name, too ! Don't forget that !

GWENNY. Yes, to be sure, you did. . . .

TALLANT. I don't deny I used to be a bit off-hand about paying my rent. I've done it often, and got into plenty of trouble through it, too ! Wouldn't you expect that of a friend of Chris's ?

(*Both laugh.*)

I wouldn't have put it beyond Chris himself !

GWENNY (*smiling*). Well, now I come to think of it, perhaps I was wrong thinking wrong things, and acting so old-fashioned with you, and all. . . . (*Forgetting her suspicions in her pleasure.*) Did Chris really mention my name to you ? I would never have expected him to mention my name, no, indeed, never ! That wass nice of Chris !

TALLANT. Chris was fond of you.

GWENNY. Did he say that too ?

TALLANT. Over and over again. Weren't you fond of him ?

GWENNY. Mr. Brown, he wass the only man that acted serious with me, and talked to me serious. Not that he talked so much, neither, but what he said wass proper on the point. . . . And to think of you being James Brown ! It certainly iss a pleasure to make your acquaintance ! I never expected to meet you, dear annwyl, no, never ! Don't you think that we had better shake hands on it ?

(*They shake hands.*)

Sit you down, Mr. Brown, and I will sit down with you.

(*She pulls the armchair to* c. *and sits.* TALLANT *sits on the chair* L. *of the table.*)

Mrs. Haggett does not like the servants sitting in the sitting-room ; she iss very English that way. Proper towny, she iss. . . . Well, whatever, she issn't home, and what she doesn't know won't hurt her. . . . (*Her eyes shining as they take him in.*) Well, well, James Brown, well ! Dear annwyl, that name brings things back to my mind, it does indeed !

TALLANT. What kind of things ?

GWENNY (*laughing*). Oh, this, and that !

TALLANT. Chris told me that you were the only one who ever liked his painting, or realized what he was getting at.

GWENNY (*nodding with delight*). Oh, yes, I liked them. Of course, I had to learn to like them. But he learned me. Oh, he learned me a lot of things ! And there wassn't nothing about him, Mistar Brown—not one thing at all, that I did not like.

TALLANT (*leaning forward, lighlty*). If you liked his pictures so much, why didn't you take better care of them ? Why did you. let so many of them get lost ?

(*She draws back.*)

GWENNY (*casually*). Now, I would rather not examine that problem, if you don't mind, Mr. Brown.

(*There is a pause.*)

TALLANT (*quickly recovering*). He taught you things, you said ?

GWENNY. Oh, yes, he teached me ! Not that he made out to be a teacher. But you could not be with him, like, and not pick up a bit here and a bit there.

TALLANT. What did he teach you ? I'd be interested to hear, if you remember.

GWENNY (*only too eager to tell*). Oh, I remember ! It wass mostly things to see, I suppose. Like the rust colour that the wet fields turn into at this time of the year, (*pointing to the platter on the corner cabinet*) when the sky turns into the colour of that old blue plate . . . (*adding proudly*) That, Mistar Brown, iss cobalt blue ! That iss a painting term, cobalt blue. And he showed me the old red barn, and the stone bridge that he wass always at it painting, and there was I all the time used to that Grassmere bridge, and never noticed it before ! He learned me that old chairs can be more than old chairs just fit to throw away. That some of them can be beautiful. He used to say them very words about the old doors in the brick houses across the fields by Morston Green there. That wass when the County Council started to take the old doors out and put the new ones in, ordered from Lewis's, Liverpool. They have got everything in Lewis's, Mistar Brown, you would be surprised. . . . And did you know that old brick houses issn't red,

but mostly green and brown ? And that moonlight and snow
issn't white at all, but all sorts of colours ? And that ash trees iss
most *decorative* when their leaves come off ? He learned me l
(*Her reminiscence becomes more personal.*) He learned me that a
man can get drunk, and not be no different, only just more so ;
and that everybody hass got more good things in them than bad
things. Oh, he learned me a big lot ! And I have never forgot
none of it, never. I have lived over and over again the time that
he wass here. Over and over again, since he died.

(*There is a pause. Then* TALLANT *cautiously leads up to the point
again :*)

TALLANT.   Did he leave you much to remember him by ?
GWENNY.   But I wass just telling you !
TALLANT.   But I was thinking of more substantial things.
GWENNY (*not understanding*).   Substantial ?
TALLANT (*as though accepting a correction*).   You're right there,
Gwenny. Our memories are the most substantial things we have.
They are the only things nobody can take away from us. Still, there
are other kinds . . . souvenirs. . . .
GWENNY (*almost to herself*).   I was wondering to myself about
the memories. I know that nobody can take them away from us.
But what happens to them when we take them away from the
place where they belong ? Don't you think, Mistar Brown, that
they get . . . left behind ? (*Pulling her chair nearer him.*) I have
been worried about that cwestiwn lately, Mistar Brown.
TALLANT.   Why have you ?
GWENNY.   Because I am going away from here. I am going to
Manchester, this afternoon. My poor brother Idwal's wife died and
left him with four small children, pethau bach. I have got to go.
It iss the will of God. But I don't want to go in the least little bit.
(*Laughing.*) Mistar and Mrs. Haggett think it iss because of them !
TALLANT.   I shouldn't worry. You'll carry your memories with
you wherever you go.
GWENNY (*looking away*).   But I won't see the red barn no more,
nor the stone bridge on the Grassmere road, nor the cornfield by
Briar Turnpike, nor any of them !
TALLANT.   The places he liked to paint . . .
GWENNY (*leaning forward*).   Yes. I used to take him a cup of
hot tea when he wass painting.
TALLANT.   And you knitted a sweater for him !
GWENNY.   Oh, did he write a letter to you about that sweater ?
TALLANT.   You must know he'd have written me everything !
GWENNY.   Everything about me ?
TALLANT.   I was his closest friend.
GWENNY (*after a pause*).   I wass pretty, once.
TALLANT (*playfully*).   You don't need to explain.
GWENNY.   I am not ashame', Mistar Brown. Only I would

prefer that you did not speak about it to Doctor Haggett or Mrs. Haggett or the two Miss Haggetts. You know the way people looked on him here—him being only an artist, and everything. They never did· understand him. And they would not understand him no better, neither, with knowing that he liked me ! And I wass wanting to keep their good opinion of me, and my place here with Doctor Haggett. But I am not ashame', no, really I am not.

TALLANT. I wouldn't tell, Gwenny.—I'll respect your memories. . . . But you must have things of his too. Little sketches, for instance.

GWENNY (*proudly*). I could show you something a lot better than sketches.

TALLANT. Oh ? What would that be ?

GWENNY. He painted a picture of me. Life-size. (*She moves her left hand up to indicate the size of the portrait.*) It hass hung over my bed all these years.

TALLANT. I should certainly like to see that, Gwenny ! Gwenny, show me the portrait ! Show it to me now !

GWENNY (*rising*). I will show it to you. (*She replaces the armchair L.C.*) It iss that portrait that makes me feel worst about leaving here. (*Starting towards the kitchen.*) You have got to come to my room to see it. It is out that way.

(*He rises and follows her. She stops abruptly as she nears the door, and turns to him.*)

Oh, I forgot !

TALLANT. Is there somebody out there ?

GWENNY. That towny maid that hass come to take my place. I wouldn't like her seeing me taking a man into my bedroom where I live for fifteen years !

TALLANT (*smiling*). What harm would that do ?

GWENNY. She would tell on me to Mrs. Haggett.

TALLANT (*moving away L. a few steps*). Oh, yes, *I* would rather Doctor and Mrs. Haggett didn't know about our talk. When can I see you again ?

GWENNY (*taking a step after him*). Where are you lodging ?

TALLANT. Down at the " Eccleston Arms." Can you come there ?

GWENNY. It iss just by the station. I will call in there on my way, after dinner, even though it iss a public-house.

TALLANT. Thank you, Gwenny. And bring the portrait with you !

GWENNY. What do you say ? That great big portrait ?

TALLANT. Gwenny, if you ever need money . . . I'm not a rich man, you know that, but these last few years I've been doing a bit better, and—and as I say, if ever you are in need, I'd buy anything of Chris's that you have to sell.

GWENNY (*quickly*). I would not sell nothing, Mistar Brown.

TALLANT. Not to a stranger, Gwenny. I know you wouldn't.
But to his friend. In memory of him and the old days. . . .

GWENNY. Duwedd annwyl, I could not take money for the
things that he leave behind.

TALLANT. Think it over, Gwenny. (*He takes a step up and looks
away.*) I'm trying to get all his pictures together in one place,
where they'll keep each other company.

GWENNY. Oh, iss that what you are doing ?

(*He turns to her as she follows up a step.*)

Oh, I think that iss a proper grand thing for you to be doing !
Well, I could not sell nothing, but I might give you——

TALLANT (*too quickly, breathlessly*). What ? The portrait ?

GWENNY (*startled*). Oh, I did not mean that ! I would have
to think a long time before I would part with that !

TALLANT (*pressing her*). Of course you would ! But to his best
friend !

GWENNY. Well, if it wass anybody in this world besides you . . .

(*She turns at the sound of a door closing off R.*)

Here iss one of them coming in through the kitchen now.

(TALLANT *goes up to the medical cabinet and gets his hat there as*
GWENNY *crosses to the kitchen door.*)

TALLANT (*turning to her*). Gwenny, I'm counting on you.

GWENNY. All right. . . . You had better be going if you don't
want them to be seeing you. . . .

(*As he goes out into the hall,* GWENNY *quickly crosses above the table
to him.*)

And, Mistar Brown ! . . . Don't tell nobody what you know
about Chris and me, there iss a nice man.

(*He pats her on the arm and goes out through the front door. He
passes the window.*
GWENNY *re-enters the room and goes to above the desk, moving
the armchair further up.*
SUSAN *comes quickly down the stairs.*)

SUSAN. That wasn't Mother, was it, Gwenny ?

GWENNY (*startled*). No. It wasn't nobody worth talking about,
really.

(BRUCE *comes in from the kitchen.*)

Now, now, I have not got no time for . . .

SUSAN (*seeing* BRUCE). Watch the front door, Gwenny !

(*She goes quickly below the table to* BRUCE, *who takes a few steps towards
her. They kiss.*)

GWENNY. You are taking a risk something terrible! You cannot get me mixed up in all this, my last day. Susan, what iss he doing here? (*She moves to behind the armchair.*)

SUSAN. I saw him standing by the shed.

BRUCE. I saw ye waving. What are ye wantin', Susan?

GWENNY. What are you hanging around our shed for, Bruce McRae? There will be a terrible row, that iss what there will be!

BRUCE. I had something I wanted to tell her.

SUSAN. What? What was it, Bruce?

BRUCE. I just come to an important decision in my life.

GWENNY (*advancing, interested, down to below and* L. *of them*). You just come to an important what, Bruce?

SUSAN (*turning to* GWENNY). Watch the front door, Gwenny!

GWENNY. How can I watch the front door when Bruce gets me so interested?

BRUCE. It's none of yer business, ye sully Welshwoman.

GWENNY. I would not be so interested if it was, ye rude Scotch boy. (*She goes huffily up above the desk to the window.*) If you do not want me to hear, however——

SUSAN. Oh, we haven't any secrets from you, Gwenny! What is it, Bruce?

BRUCE. Bertie Willis has been naggin' at me to sell ma' business, so he can have all the contractin' between Childer Barnston and Grove End. He only wants to pay me sixty pounds.

SUSAN. Well?

BRUCE. Well, it's nae enough, but I've made up me mind to take it.

(GWENNY *turns and looks at them.*)

SUSAN. But what did you want to do that for, Bruce?

BRUCE. So that I can get to Chelsea and study art.

GWENNY. Chelsea? Where iss that?

BRUCE. It's a village near London that's chock-fule o' artists.

GWENNY. That doesn't sound so tempting, neither.

BRUCE. Well, I'm going.

SUSAN. I think it's a terribly hasty thing to do, Bruce. (*She drops her head.*) And it means you'll be going right away from Childer Barnston . . .

BRUCE. I wouldna done it, only on one condition.

SUSAN. And what's that?

BRUCE. You've got to come wi' me.

SUSAN. Bruce, you know Mummy would never let me go! Didn't you hear the way she was scolding this morning?

BRUCE. I wasna countin' on lettin' your mother know anything aboot it.

(GWENNY *moves to above the armchair.*)

GWENNY. Bruce McRae ! You are not planning in your mind to elope !

BRUCE. Well, crike, if Susan likes me as much as she says she does, she won't risk letting me go off wi'out her.

(SUSAN *admits as much by taking his hand.*)

GWENNY. Ass if there wassn't enough happening in this house this morning, without you draggin' in this eloping talk, and getting Susan all upset again ! Her mam got me proper wild this morning, and I am going to show her ! And there issn't no use of me wasting any time about her——

SUSAN. Oh, Bruce, I think you're wonderful, really I do !

(*He smiles, she turns to* GWENNY.)

Don't you, Gwenny ?

GWENNY. I think he wants putting in his place, but I do look up to him for it, I must say. (*She moves to the window, then back to above the desk.*)

BRUCE (*to* SUSAN). You give your clo'es to Gwenny to take with her to Manchester to-night ; then I'll bring the pony trap here to fetch Gwenny's box. And you'll come along wi' me, the same as if ye was seeing her off, and then I drive ye doon to Rocklands station and dump ye in the train. And then I'll meet the both o' ye in Manchester. And then we get married ! I don't think there's much wrong with that plan !

GWENNY. Susan ! If you listen to one word more of this, I will go straight and tell on you to your mam.

SUSAN (*frightened*). Gwenny, you wouldn't do that !

(GWENNY *moves down to below the armchair.*)

GWENNY. Why wouldn't I ? It iss my Bible duty !

SUSAN (*pleading*). You told me you hadn't got anything against artists. . . .

GWENNY. I have not got anything, but all the people round here have.

SUSAN. Haven't you ever cared an awful lot for somebody, Gwenny ?

GWENNY. Do you think that I would be watching this front door if I hadn't ? (*She crosses to above the table.*)

BRUCE. Hoots, Gwenny, say ye'll help her !

GWENNY. And if I do help her, it will not be on your account, my lad ! When a girl gets into the flurried state that you've got Susan into, she needs somebody to look after her, and see that she does get married, and not go off her head regardless. I have been in love myself, and I know.

(*The front-door bell rings. They freeze—all three.*)

You better get off the premises now, Bruce McRae, before they nab you ! (*She goes above the desk to the window and looks out.*)

BRUCE (*taking a step* R.). I'll have the trap at the door at half-past four.

SUSAN (*moving to him*). As early as that, Bruce ?

BRUCE. It's no tu soon if Gwenny is catching the five-o'clock at Rocklands Station.

(BRUCE *and* SUSAN *kiss again.* GWENNY *turns from the window and sees them.*)

GWENNY. Will you give over doing that rubbish. . . . (*To* SUSAN.) You get upstairs and get yourself ready.

BRUCE. Half-past four, on the dot !

(*He goes out through the kitchen, closing the door after him.*)

GWENNY. If you let your mam and dad see you in this state . . .

(SUSAN *runs into the hall and disappears up the stairs.*)

(*Going into the hall to the front door.*) What iss come over this house this morning, that iss what I want to know. . . .

(*She opens the front door and admits* ROSEN, *an oily and too affable London Jew of middle age. He is wearing a smart light-coloured lounge suit under a spring overcoat.*)

ROSEN (*outside*). This is where Doctor Haggett lives, I believe ? (*He has a fairly marked suburban Cockney accent.*)

GWENNY. It iss where he has been living for thirty years.

ROSEN (*stepping inside*). I wonder if I can see him for a moment ?

GWENNY. You could see him if he wass here, but he iss not here.

ROSEN. Will he be long ?

GWENNY. Not so very long, I should think. The Haggett family is in to their food always on the dot.

ROSEN. In that case, I'll come in and wait, then, if you'll allow me.

(*He hands her his light grey homburg hat, then enters the room.*)

GWENNY. Watch yourself for the paint ! (*She closes the front door and puts his hat on the hall table just off* L.)

ROSEN. I'm used to paint.

(*He looks about the room, still in his overcoat.* GWENNY *comes in and crosses to behind the armchair and watches him. He turns and meets her gaze.*)

You must be Gwenny.

GWENNY (*surprised*). You do not know me !

ROSEN. No, but I've heard an awful lot about you !

GWENNY (*taking a step nearer to him*). What did you hear and where did you hear it ?

Rosen. Well, I heard you've got a kind nature, and appreciate modern painting. . . .

Gwenny (*sitting at the desk*). I will see if I can get the Doctor on the telephone. . . . He should never have put his foot outside this house to-day ! (*She picks up* Dr. Haggett's *call-book.*)

Rosen. Don't hurry him, Gwenny. Let me enjoy myself. Well, I've seen the " old brick house fronts " on the way to Morston Green . . .

(*She looks at him.*)

And I've seen " the red barn " behind this house . . . and now I've seen you ; only I expected you'd be wearing a gingham dress.

Gwenny (*questioning*). A gingham dress ?

Rosen. Red and white checked gingham, the same as you used to wear.

Gwenny. What do you know about what I used to wear——

(Dr. Haggett, Mrs. Haggett *and* Ada *enter by the front door.* Mrs. Haggett *and* Ada *go upstairs.* Dr. Haggett *places his hat and bag on the table in the hall.* Gwenny *rises and crosses into the hall to* R. *of him.*)

Oh, Doctor, I am not sorry to see you reach home, indeed I am not. There is too many things going on around here that iss beyond my understanding. I think the best thing for me is to get back into my back-kitchen, and stay there !

(*She disappears along the passage to off* R. Dr. Haggett *looks after her, puzzled, then comes into the room to* L. *of* Rosen.)

Rosen (*taking a step up*). So this is Doctor Haggett ?

Dr. Haggett (*nodding his head*). And what can I do for you ?

Rosen. My card.

(*He presents it.* Dr. Haggett *looks at it, then turns and crosses towards his desk, gesturing meanwhile to the chair below the desk.*)

Dr. Haggett. A patient ?

Rosen. No, no !

Dr. Haggett (*as* Rosen *shakes his head*). Oh ! Sit down, Mr. . . . Rosen. (*He points to the armchair and seats himself at the desk.*)

Rosen. Thank you. (*He brings the armchair down a little.*)

(Rosen *sits.* Dr. Haggett *begins arranging his vest and tie, paying scant heed to* Rosen.)

Doctor Haggett, in the course of your professional career, you once had as a patient a young friend of mine. A painter . . .

(Dr. Haggett *shifts his chair forward, staring at* Rosen *in amazement.*)

. . . A painter with whom, I confess, I had personal difficulties.

Ten years ago, his death left me with that deep pang we all feel in such cases. Just lately, I came across some letters. . . . Letters he wrote to me while he lived here, under your care. They gave me an idea how, in a small way, I might ease my conscience as regards him. Doctor Haggett, my friend Christopher Bean died owing you twenty pounds. I've totted up the interest on the unpaid bill at six per cent, and the total for ten years comes to exactly thirty-three pounds four shillings and sevenpence halfpenny. Allow me to offer you my cheque for the sum.

(*He presents the cheque.* DR. HAGGETT *nods his head, takes the cheque and reads it.*)

DR. HAGGETT (*almost breathless*). Thank you very much, sir.

ROSEN. Don't mention it. In paying this, I fulfil a sacred duty to a poor devil that I might have given a hand to before he passed beyond all human aid. Of course, I know we're all mortal, but I shall go back to London feeling . . .

DR. HAGGETT. A happier man ?

ROSEN. You take the words out of my mouth, Doctor Haggett.

DR. HAGGETT (*pocketing the cheque*). Mr. Rosen, I'm delighted to make your acquaintance ; and I see that artists make better paying patients than I thought. But there's a question I'd like to put to you.

ROSEN. Don't hesitate, Dr. Haggett ! Anything !

DR. HAGGETT (*timorous*). Are you, by any chance, on the point of inquiring whether Chris Bean left any pictures behind him, that you can take away as souvenirs ?

ROSEN (*protesting*). No, no, no ! I don't do things that way. I don't come begging.

DR. HAGGETT (*with humility*). My dear Mr. Rosen, I never said you did. I only asked you . . .

ROSEN (*after giving him a look, lifting his hand graciously*). Well, if you'll allow me to be business-like, I was on the point of asking you about any such pictures you may still have in your possession.

(DR. HAGGETT *sits up.*)

(*Business-like.*) I assume, of course, that they are your property. The boy had no family, and any pictures he left here—even those he did not give you personally—may be considered security for that unpaid bill, and so forfeit to you. Doctor Haggett, I'll give you two hundred pounds for the lot !

DR. HAGGETT (*stunned*). Two hundred pounds !

ROSEN. For the lot, understand.

DR. HAGGETT. For Chris Bean's pictures ?

ROSEN. I can't go any higher. I hope you don't exaggerate their value.

DR. HAGGETT (*out to front, quite voiceless*). Two hundred——

Rosen (*quickly*). That is my offer. Take it or leave it. I consider it very generous.

Dr. Haggett (*quickly*). Oh, I'm not saying a word against your offer, Mr. Rosen! The only trouble is, you're not the first. There was a gentleman here not two hours ago . . .

Rosen (*leaning forward*). With the same proposition?

Dr. Haggett (*sadly*). No—not exactly . . .

Rosen. You didn't sell *him* your Christopher Bean pictures!

Dr. Haggett. No. I gave them to him!

Rosen. What!

Dr. Haggett. There was one Chris painted of the old stone bridge on the Grassmere road . . . and another . . .

Rosen (*rising*). You gave away the " Grassmere Stone Bridge ! " Dr. Haggett, you've been swindled!

Dr. Haggett. My dear fellow, you don't need to tell me that!

Rosen. But how in God's name did you——

Dr. Haggett. He sent me a telegram from London to say he was coming.

Rosen. What was his name?

Dr. Haggett. I'm not very good at names . . . Let me see . . . (*Fumbling through his pockets.*) I ought to have his telegram somewhere, though . . . (*He sees it on the desk, and picks it up.*) Here it is. (*Reading.*) Davenport. That's it, Maxwell Davenport.

Rosen (*staggered*). Maxwell Davenport?

Dr. Haggett. Yes.

Rosen (*incredulous*). You mean to say Maxwell Davenport let you *give* him . . .

Dr. Haggett. I thought they were no good.

(Rosen *looks at* Dr. Haggett.)

He said they were no good.

Rosen (*unable to believe his hearing*). Davenport said that?

Dr. Haggett. Yes. (*Rising and giving* Rosen *the telegram.*) Here, if you don't believe me! Do you know him?

Rosen (*reading*). Do I know Davenport? Why, of course I know him! (*He moves away to* R.C.) But I would never have believed this of him. (*He sniffs the smell of powder.*) Have you got witnesses?

Dr. Haggett. I've got my wife and daughter.

Rosen (*grinning and confidential*). Then, Doctor, this may not be so serious.

(*He returns the telegram and they both sit again.*)

I think I can see how we can settle Davenport. He's the chief critic on the " English Arts Monthly," the best we have in London, and everybody licks his boots. Now he would hardly care to have it known what a dirty trick he played on you, to get those pictures free when they're worth a—(*he remembers discretion*)—two hundred pounds. So this is what we do.

(*He extracts papers from his pocket and explains*—Dr. Haggett *listening attentively.*)

I have here with me a bill of sale for what he took, all made out in advance by my solicitor.

(*The front-door bell rings.*)

You sign it, and I give you my cheque for two hundred pounds. (*Rising.*) Then we get you and your wife and daughter to go down to Chester Police Court and sign an affidavit swearing that you are telling the truth about every word the great art critic said. Especially about the pictures being no good. You leave the rest to me. I think we can cook Mr. Davenport's goose for him !

(Gwenny *passes along the passage from* R. *and goes to the front door. She admits* Maxwell Davenport, *an elderly and distinguished English gentleman. He is wearing a slightly old-fashioned cut lounge suit, a wing-collar and bow-tie, and carries a darkish overcoat.*)

Davenport (*outside*). Is Doctor Haggett in ? He's expecting me.

(*He steps into the hall.* Gwenny *shuts the door.* Davenport *comes into the room to* L. *of the table.*
Dr. Haggett *looks up.* Rosen *silences him with a gesture.* Gwenny *enters and comes down to* R. *of* Davenport.)

Gwenny. The Doctor hass got a gentleman with him. (*She indicates the chair* L. *of the table.*) Will you sit yourself, and have a bit of a rest, yes ?

(*She moves away to above the table.* Rosen *recognizes* Davenport, *smiles, and moves up to the corner cabinet and stands with his back partly to* Davenport.)

Davenport. Oh, thank you. That's very kind of you. You're not by any chance the famous Gwenny ?

(*There is a pause.*)

Gwenny (*practically annihilated*). Does everybody in London know me ?

Davenport. Then you are Gwenny ! What luck that you're still here ! The Grassmere stone bridge, the brick houses on the Morston Green road, the old red barn, and now, Gwenny herself ! (*He places his coat over the back of the chair* L. *of the table.*)

Gwenny (*crossing to behind the chair* R. *of the table*). Doctor Haggett, I cannot stand no longer to have strange English people coming into here and calling me by my Christian name! (*She crosses towards the kitchen door.*)

DAVENPORT. Don't be alarmed, please, Gwenny.

(GWENNY *goes out into the kitchen in a panic, and closes the door.* DAVENPORT *turns and moves a few steps towards* DR. HAGGETT.)

Is this Doctor Haggett?

DR. HAGGETT. Yes, it is.

DAVENPORT. I'm Davenport.

DR. HAGGETT (*rising—sharply*). Who?

DAVENPORT. Maxwell Davenport. I sent you a telegram yesterday from London. Don't let me disturb you, though . . . (*He moves up a step as he indicates* ROSEN.) . . . I'll wait outside.

DR. HAGGETT (*taking a step towards him*). No, no, no! Don't go!

(*He turns and crosses to* ROSEN. DAVENPORT *goes back to the chair* L. *of the table.*)

(L. *of* ROSEN *whispering.*) Is *this* Davenport?

ROSEN (*nodding*). Yes. It's Davenport.

DR. HAGGETT. But it isn't the same chap!

ROSEN. What!

DR. HAGGETT. It isn't the same chap, I tell you! And if this is Davenport, who in Heaven's name was the other one?

ROSEN (*speaking quickly to* DR. HAGGETT *as he calms him*). Don't say any more for the present, Doctor Haggett. . . . (*Confidentially.*) Not another word . . . Wait till we find out how we stand. (*He pockets his papers hastily, and turns, smirking.*)

DAVENPORT (R.C., *turning round*). Rosen! (*In disgust.*) May I ask what the devil you're doing here?

ROSEN (*crossing to* DAVENPORT). Do you think you ought to swear at me, Mr. Davenport? You've got no excuse for swearing at me in public! Print what you like about me, but don't insult me to my face! (*He crosses* L.)

DAVENPORT (R.C.). I might have known the scavengers would be gathering. (*He turns to* DR. HAGGETT, *who makes a strong gesture.*) I beg your pardon, Doctor, but this man, who exploits artists and treats their work as so much merchandise . . .

ROSEN (L., *cringing*). It's not the artists I exploit. It's the customers. And it's men like me that justify the existence of you art critics! Where would you be, writing about your tactile values, your limpid shadows, and your something-or-other high lights, if you didn't have us to create interest in art by building up prices?

DAVENPORT. You befoul the whole business of dealing in art with your tricks and forgeries. . . .

ROSEN. Tricks and forgeries! (*He snorts and turns away up* L.)

DR. HAGGETT (*floundering—coming down* C.). Just a minute,

just a minute. This is my house, and I have a right to know what's going on here !

(ROSEN *returns to behind the armchair.*)

You say you're Mr. Davenport. Mr. Rosen says you are. All right, then, you must be Mr. Davenport. But will you in Heaven's name tell me what this is all about ?

DAVENPORT (R.). It's about one of the world's greatest injustices, Doctor, which I am doing my small part to set right. You once had for your patient a poor boy, a painter . . .

DR. HAGGETT (R.C.). Yes, I know. Chris Bean.

DAVENPORT (*surprised*). Oh, I'm glad you remember him, Doctor. Now this boy I mention . . .

DR. HAGGETT (*breaking in, pointing his finger at* DAVENPORT'S *chest*). Died owing me twenty pounds, and you've come here to pay it !

DAVENPORT. No, Doctor! No ! Don't say that Bean owed any man anything ! (*Tapping* DR. HAGGETT *on the shoulder with his left hand.*) It is we, all of us, who stand in everlasting debt to him ! As the world always stands in debt to its men of genius !

DR. HAGGETT. Genius ? Chris Bean a . . .

(*He turns, moves towards his desk, stops, turns, and motions* DAVEN-PORT *to be seated in the armchair.* DAVENPORT *crosses and sits.* DR. HAGGETT *sits at his desk.*)

DAVENPORT. Thank you ! (*More quietly.*) Well, Doctor, I've come here to gather any details I may find concerning his life here, for a critical biography of him I am writing.

DR. HAGGETT. You're writing a book about Chris Bean !

DAVENPORT. That is my occupation at the moment, yes.

DR. HAGGETT. Why ?

DAVENPORT. Haven't you read about the sensation his pictures have been making in London and New York ?

(ROSEN *gives* DAVENPORT *a look of annoyance.* DR. HAGGETT *shakes his head dizzily.*)

Haven't you seen the current number of the " London Mercury " ?

ROSEN (*taking a step down*). That only came out yesterday, Mr. Davenport.

DAVENPORT. Quite.

(ROSEN *moves up to above the desk and takes out his cigarette-case.*)

Well, Doctor Haggett, art is long, and the world is often slow to recognize it. Only now, ten years after his death, has Christopher Bean had his first London exhibition, at the Leicester Galleries. Only now do we realize that he was not merely the greatest English painter, but one of the greatest masters of all time.

DR. HAGGETT. Our Chris Bean was ?

DAVENPORT. Your Chris Bean, who painted and drank and coughed his short life away, here in Childer Barnston! The place from which he wrote to his friend James Brown—alas, also dead—the exquisite group of letters published yesterday in the " London Mercury."

(ROSEN *lights a cigarette.*)

DR. HAGGETT. Our Christopher Bean!

(*There is a pause. Then light dawns, and he looks at* ROSEN, *who looks away.*)

(*Turning in his swivel chair to face down stage.*) So those were the letters you chaps kept coming across!

(MRS. HAGGETT *comes downstairs. She is wearing a coat, which matches her skirt, over her blouse.*)

ROSEN. You guessed right, Doctor.

(DR. HAGGETT *gives him an indignant look, then turns and sees his wife.*)

DR. HAGGETT. Hannah, for God's sake, come in here!

(MRS. HAGGETT *comes down to* R. *of* DAVENPORT, *who rises.*)

(*Introducing.*) My wife—Mr. Davenport.

MRS. HAGGETT (*starting*). Mr. Davenport?

DR. HAGGETT (*quickly*). That's all right, Hannah. I'll explain later. And Mr. Rosen. (*Turning to* DAVENPORT *with simple dignity.*) Mr. Davenport, we live a long way from London.

(ADA *comes downstairs.*)

I am only a simple country doctor, but I confess, much as I liked Chris Bean, I never thought he'd get anywhere in this world. Never.

(ADA *enters slowly, her ears pricked as usual, and crosses to above the table.*)

DAVENPORT. Well, I'm not exaggerating, Doctor, when I say that no painter of our time has got as far as he has.

MRS. HAGGETT (*dumfounded*). Does this mean people are actually *paying* money for Chris Bean's pictures?

DAVENPORT (*to her, quickly*). If only the dealers could find more to sell! There are so few that they fetch high prices even in these days.

ADA. As much as twelve guineas?

DAVENPORT. My dear young lady! Not less than one thousand, and as much as two thousand.

MRS. HAGGETT. Two thousand what?

DAVENPORT. Why, guineas!

ADA. Two . . . thousand . . . guineas . . . each!

DR. HAGGETT (*to* ROSEN). And you offered me a paltry two hundred pounds for the lot !

ROSEN. You keep in mind I wasn't the first, and say no more about it.

DAVENPORT. A very generous offer . . . for Mr. Rosen. I hope I arrived in time to stop his game.

(DR. HAGGETT *turns away, dazed.*)

MRS. HAGGETT (*in a sudden scream of anguish*). Oh !

DR. HAGGETT. What is it, Hannah ?

MRS. HAGGETT. . . . I . . . I don't feel very well . . .

(*She sits on the chair* L. *of the table, looking before her in horror.* ADA *sits on the chair above the table. In the meantime,* GWENNY *enters along the passage from off* R. *and enters the room.*)

GWENNY (*crossing down to above* DR. HAGGETT). Another telegram for you, Doctor Haggett. (*She holds it out in her hand.*)

DR. HAGGETT (*weakly*). Another telegram ?

(*He takes it and opens it, then puts on his spectacles.* GWENNY *goes out up* C., *and disappears along the passage to* R.)

DAVENPORT (*up* C.). Now, really, Rosen, I do think you might have gone higher than two hundred.

ROSEN (*pleasantly*). I'm not a rich man, Mr. Davenport, and I've got a pretty small business. The Fulham Road is a threepenny 'bus ride from Bond Street, you know.

DAVENPORT. That may be, but I advise you to stick to your forgeries. They're more respectable than swindling honest men who aren't equipped to defend themselves. (*To* DR. HAGGETT, *crisply.*) Now, Doctor ! I don't usually mix in buying and selling, but to protect you, I will gladly put the proper values on any Christopher Beans that you may have.

DR. HAGGETT (*breaking in, haggard as he looks from the telegram in his hands*). Would you mind, sir, explaining this telegram to me ?

DAVENPORT. Let me see it . . . (*He takes it. Then as he reads the telegram.*) Why, it's clear enough. The Tate Gallery—(*He looks at* DR. HAGGETT) that's in London, you know. (*He looks at the telegram again.*) The Tate Gallery offers you fifteen hundred guineas for the choice of your Christopher Bean canvases. (*He returns the telegram to* DR. HAGGETT.)

DR. HAGGETT (*quietly, after a pause*). Mr. Davenport, you see in me a desperate man.

DAVENPORT. Desperate, Doctor ? The owner of pictures worth a fortune ?

DR. HAGGETT. How do you know I've got any such pictures ?

DAVENPORT. From the "London Mercury "! Bean, in his letters—

(DR. HAGGETT *looks up and winces.*)

—enumerates seven of the pictures he painted and left behind him here. The "Briar Turnpike Cornfield," "The Grassmere Stone Bridge," "The Old Red Barn," "The Brick Houses" . . .

DR. HAGGETT (*breaking in*). I suppose the whole trouble is I didn't take them seriously enough. . . .

DAVENPORT. Don't reproach yourself, Doctor. You weren't the only one.

(DR. HAGGETT *draws in his breath and gives him an agonized look.*)

(*Suddenly alarmed.*) Doctor, for God's sake! You haven't let anything happen to them!

(MRS. HAGGETT *feels even worse.*)

DR. HAGGETT (*rising and crossing* C., *in despair*). They must be somewhere! There are those two, of course. . . . But if he left seven. . . . Did you ever hear of people throwing away oil paintings? Valuable oil paintings? . . . (*Setting his teeth, grimly, rallying.*) I'm going to look for those pictures. And I'm going to find them! And when I do find them, I'll pay them the honour they deserve. (*He turns around, pointing to the walls.*) I'll hang them on my walls. Now I come to think of it, I don't think I'm so keen in parting with them. Not now I know their worth. . . . (*Glaring at* ROSEN.) At least, not for the paltry sums I've been offered. (*Dropping into his chair at the desk, exhaustedly.*) But now, I'd like you all to go away and leave me to eat my dinner in peace, and talk matters over with my family. This is all very, very sudden. I've got to put my thinking-cap on.

DAVENPORT (*below the armchair, still anxious*). But you'll let me come in again this afternoon?

DR. HAGGETT. What for?

DAVENPORT. Why, to get your recollections of Bean's life here! (*He turns and goes to the chair where* MRS. HAGGETT *is sitting.*)

DR. HAGGETT (*suffering*). After I've had my dinner.

(DAVENPORT *tries to pick up his coat and move away, but* MRS. HAGGETT *is seated on part of it. He stops and turns to her.*)

DAVENPORT. Oh, excuse me.

(*She barely rises, and does not look at him.* DAVENPORT *draws his overcoat from beneath her.*)

Thank you.

(*As he moves towards* DR. HAGGETT, *he takes a copy of the "London Mercury" from a pocket in his coat.*)

Let me leave this copy of the "London Mercury" with you. You'll find Bean's letters in it. (*He opens it and finds the place.*) I brought it for the list of pictures he mentions. (*He holds it out to* DR. HAGGETT *and returns to* C.) But you'll enjoy reading what he says about *you.*

DR. HAGGETT. Thank you very much. (*He lays the open magazine down on his desk.*)

DAVENPORT (*looking around, embarrassed*). Well, good-bye.

(*He goes. The moment the front door closes,* ROSEN *goes into the hall. He makes sure the coast is clear, then returns to above* DR. HAGGETT.)

ROSEN. Now about that man who was here before me. If you don't know his real name, what did he look like ?

DR. HAGGETT. You buzz off too. (*He kicks weakly with his right foot.*)

ROSEN. All right, Doctor. All right ! (*He goes to the hall and gets his hat.*) But I'll turn up again, don't you worry. (*He looks into the room.*) And don't you do anything final till you see me.

(*He goes out, and is seen passing the window.* ADA *stands up and looks at the patch over the mantelpiece where the picture was. There is a pause.*)

DR. HAGGETT. The one chance I ever had in my life to make any money, and it's slipped through my fingers !

ADA (*going up a step*). I can't look at that spot on the wall where my picture was, without boiling over !

MRS. HAGGETT. I think I'll go upstairs and lie down for a bit. (*She rises, and starts wearily for the stairs.*)

(GWENNY *enters from the kitchen, closes the door and moves to* R. *of the table. She takes the flower-bowl to the sideboard, then begins removing the cover.*)

GWENNY. Well, now that all those funny Londoners iss gone, I suppose I better lay the table for your dinner, all of you.

MRS. HAGGETT (*her back to the audience—weakly*). I don't want any dinner.

(GWENNY *folds the table-cover.*)

DR. HAGGETT (*indignantly*). You don't ! You don't ! Who's to blame for this ?

(GWENNY *looks up, astonished.*)

MRS. HAGGETT (*turning to him*). You can't blame me !

(ADA *sits on the chair above the table.*)

DR. HAGGETT. Which of us was it took him in, and gave him the old shed to paint in ?

MRS. HAGGETT. You had no more use for his pictures than I had !

(GWENNY *crosses to the sideboard and opens the drawer.*)

GWENNY.   I cannot have you two people having a row like this on my last day !   (*She puts the cover in the drawer.*)

DR. HAGGETT.   Mrs. Haggett and I will have a row if we want to, without any help from you, young woman !

GWENNY (*slamming the sideboard drawer shut*).   Doctor Haggett, you have not ever spoke to me like that before !

DR. HAGGETT (*practically screaming*).   Get back to your kitchen.

(GWENNY *runs for her life into the kitchen.*)

I can't stand any more talk !

ADA.   Now the important thing is for us not to lose our heads. There are only two things that matter. The first man was not Mr. Davenport. And if it wasn't, who was he ?

MRS. HAGGETT (*up C., with her back to* DR. HAGGETT).   What does that matter ? Your father gave the pictures to him.

ADA.   It matters a lot.   He got those pictures out of Daddy on —on false pretences.

DR. HAGGETT.   Hannah, Ada's right ! He did !

MRS. HAGGETT (*turning to* DR. HAGGETT).   Then we can get them back !

DR. HAGGETT.   If it wasn't for that twelve guineas he gave to Ada.

ADA.   That twelve guineas wasn't for the back side of the picture.

MRS. HAGGETT (*crossing down to* R. *of* DR. HAGGETT).   You must find him, Arthur.

DR. HAGGETT.   But I don't know what his real name is ! All I know is he's gone back to London a happier man . . . (*He rises, then through his teeth.*) I will find him, though, somehow ! And when I do, I'll give him the hiding he deserves.   (*He strides to and fro as he forms his plan.*)

MRS. HAGGETT.   He's younger than you, Arthur. Perhaps he'll give you the hiding.

DR. HAGGETT (*striding to and fro*).   Very well, then.   I'll get a solicitor.   (*He crosses to the desk and lifts the telephone.*) I'll bring an action against him . . . (*After a pause.*) Law actions cost money if you aren't sure of winning.   (*He drops the telephone.*) It isn't as though we minded parting with what he took. . . .

MRS. HAGGETT.   No, we didn't know what they were !

DR. HAGGETT (*with a sudden shout of anguish*).   And I called both of you in to have a look at an honest man !   (*He croaks hoarsely and goes up* L.C.)

ADA.   The wicked, sneaking, thieving, greedy creature . . . it just makes me ill, that's what it does.

DR. HAGGETT (*coming down* L.C.).   Hannah, our baby girl's right. It's the greed of it that turns my stomach ! If Davenport isn't telling black lies, I allowed that greedy sinner to grab between two and four thousand pounds out of my hands.

MRS. HAGGETT (*going to him*).   Now, look here, he said he was going to go into business with you. Couldn't you tell him you refuse to have any more dealings with him unless he brings the pictures back ?

ADA (*scornfully*). Yes, but all that nonsense about business was just to lead poor Daddy up the garden path——

DR. HAGGETT. And not so much of the " poor Daddy," my girl !

MRS. HAGGETT. Oh, the wicked, scheming, greedy . . .

ADA (*to* DR. HAGGETT). How many pictures did Chris Bean leave here ?

(MRS. HAGGETT'S *strange alarm revives.*)

DR. HAGGETT. Davenport said it was seven.

ADA. And you said people don't throw away oil paintings. Well, what's become of the other five ?

DR. HAGGETT. Gwenny ! (*To* MRS. HAGGETT.) Hannah, a baby girl has got more in her head than both of us put together !

(GWENNY *comes back from the kitchen.*)

Gwenny, are you sure you had a thorough go at that attic ?

GWENNY (*in the doorway, frightened*). The attic, Doctor Haggett ?

DR. HAGGETT. When that first gentleman came here ?

GWENNY. Yes, sure, Doctor Haggett.

DR. HAGGETT. And you saw no sign whatever of any pictures up there ?

GWENNY. Nothing whatever in this world, Doctor Haggett.

DR. HAGGETT. Go back to your kitchen.

(GWENNY *goes as before, closing the door.*)

Ada, you go and look, there's a dear.

(ADA *runs upstairs.*)

(*He crosses up and calls again.*) Susan ! Come down here a minute.

MRS. HAGGETT. What do you want Susan for, Arthur ? (*She sits on the chair* L. *of the table.*)

DR. HAGGETT (*moving down to his desk*). We haven't asked Susan yet. She may know something.

(SUSAN *comes downstairs, in evident alarm, and enters to up* C.)

SUSAN (*frightened*). What is it, Daddy ? What do you want ?

DR. HAGGETT. Have you seen any old pictures of Chris Bean's hanging about ?

SUSAN (*relieved*). Oh, is that all ! (*She moves away to above the table.*)

DR. HAGGETT (*crossing to* L. *of her*). Is that all ! Is that all ! What are you blithering about ?

SUSAN (*turning to him*). Daddy, what's come over you all of a sudden, screaming your head off like this ?

DR. HAGGETT. Answer my question !

SUSAN. Yes, of course I have.

MRS. HAGGETT.   What ? ! }
DR. HAGGETT.   Where ? ! } *(Both speak simultaneously.)*

SUSAN. The last time I saw them, they were in the shed at the bottom of the back garden.

(MRS. HAGGETT *seems on the point of fainting.*)

DR. HAGGETT. In the shed !

SUSAN. Yes, Daddy.

DR. HAGGETT. How many ?

SUSAN. I can't remember offhand. Eight or ten, I think.

DR. HAGGETT. Eight or ten !

SUSAN. Yes. They were in the same corner where we used to keep the coal slack.

DR. HAGGETT. I'm in and out of that old shed the whole day long, (*he moves away a few steps*) taking my bike out and putting it back again, and I haven't seen any pictures ! (*He returns to* SUSAN.) When did you see them last ?

SUSAN (*guiltily*). Oh, not so long ago . . . I remember showing them to Bruce McRae.

DR. HAGGETT (*wildly excited*). Aha ! Bruce McRae. He's stolen them !

SUSAN (*indignant*). Daddy, he hasn't ! He'd never do a thing like that !

DR. HAGGETT. They were in the shed ! You showed them to him. They aren't there now. He must have stolen them !

SUSAN. No !

DR. HAGGETT. No ? Well, I'll fetch him here ! I'll telephone Maggie Frost, the Post Office, to fetch him for me ! (*He crosses quickly to the desk.*)

SUSAN (*following quickly to* R. *of him*). Daddy !

(DR. HAGGETT *snatches up the telephone.*)

MRS. HAGGETT (*suffocating*). It's no good, Arthur.

DR. HAGGETT (*sitting in the chair at the desk*). What do you mean, no good ? (*He turns to her.*)

MRS. HAGGETT. Bruce McRae didn't steal the pictures.

DR. HAGGETT. How do you know he didn't ?

MRS. HAGGETT. I burnt them.

(*There is a pause—as he looks at her, speechless with horror.*)

DR. HAGGETT. You what !

MRS. HAGGETT. I put them on a bonfire, and burnt them.

DR. HAGGETT. The whole eight or ten ?

MRS. HAGGETT. I should have said there were more.

DR. HAGGETT (*no longer able to control himself*). You would have said there were more ! At two thousand guineas each ! You would have said there were more !

MRS. HAGGETT.   You thought they were terrible pictures too, Arthur.

DR. HAGGETT (*screaming*).   Don't keep on saying that, woman !

(SUSAN *moves from the desk to above the armchair* L.C.)

Hannah, you ought to go down on your knees, and pray for the forgiveness of both your children !   (*After a moment his eye falls upon the magazine lying on his desk—He picks it up and begins to glance through it.*)

(ADA *comes downstairs and enters to* L. *of* MRS. HAGGETT.)

ADA.   Gwenny was right.   There isn't a single picture in that attic.

MRS. HAGGETT.   Your father knows that, Ada.   There isn't a single picture . . . anywhere.   (*Apologetically.*)   They took up so much room, I set fire to the lot.

(*There is a pause.*)

ADA.   Mummy, you didn't ! . . .   Then we'll have to work ourselves to the bone to get the two back we gave away this morning.

(DR. HAGGETT *has been studying the "London Mercury." He holds up his hand for attention.*)

(*Turning to* DR. HAGGETT.)   Daddy——   (*She breaks off as she sees his outstretched hand.*)

(SUSAN *moves nearer to* DR. HAGGETT.)

DR. HAGGETT (*reading aloud*).   "Dr. H. takes conscientious care of me.   He knows nothing of medicine, but looks like a gargoyle, and that amuses me."

SUSAN (*frightened*).   What's he saying, Mummy ?

DR. HAGGETT (*to* SUSAN, *as he points to himself*).   Doctor H. is me !   That's what Chris Bean wrote about me in his letters ! . . . (*Continuing reading.*)   " I beg him to let me do a portrait of him, but all my pleading avails me nothing.   His notion of art belongs to the lower animals."

MRS. HAGGETT.   Perhaps, if you had let him do a portrait of you, we'd be better off now.   You'd never have used a picture of yourself to stop a leak in the chicken-house.

DR. HAGGETT (*loftily holding out the magazine to* SUSAN).   You can read the rest, Susan.   Perhaps he has something kind to say about your mother.

(SUSAN *takes the magazine and sits in the armchair.* ADA *crosses to above the armchair and leans over* SUSAN'S *shoulder.* DR. HAGGETT *drops his head on his right hand.*)

SUSAN (*reading*).   " This angel of devotion is both sister and nurse to me, and more than both.   I know that her care is adding months to my life, all the more because she, and only she, sees merit in what I paint. She is the single comfort I have found in my life here, and in her own way she is beautiful ! "

(MRS. HAGGETT's *smile broadens.*)

MRS. HAGGETT (*out to front*). Well, I liked the boy, and I encouraged him !

ADA (*reading over her sister's shoulder*). But, Mummy, that wasn't you ! That was Gwenny !

(MRS. HAGGETT's *smile fades, as she looks sharply at* ADA.)

(*Reading.*) " When I go into the fields these chill autumn mornings, she brings me hot tea to drink."

MRS. HAGGETT. Our tea !

DR. HAGGETT (*slowly*). It doesn't matter now.

MRS. HAGGETT. It does matter that a boy I befriended should carry on behind my back with the servant !

SUSAN. But, Mummy, it doesn't say that !

MRS. HAGGETT. It says she was beautiful. She was never beautiful !

DR. HAGGETT (*springing to his feet again*). Good God !

ADA   ⎫(*together*).   Daddy !
SUSAN   ⎭   What is it ?

MRS. HAGGETT. Arthur, I wish you wouldn't swear so loud.

DR. HAGGETT. Chris Bean did paint another portrait while he was here ! I remember he did !

ADA. But who did he paint it of ?

DR. HAGGETT. Of Gwenny !

(*Sensation.*)

MRS. HAGGETT. Arthur, you're right. He did !

ADA. Yes, it's a great big portrait !

DR. HAGGETT. What's become of it ?

MRS. HAGGETT. It's been hanging in her room ever since he died.

DR. HAGGETT. Ada, go into Gwenny's bedroom, and see if it's still there.

(ADA *crosses above the table on her way to the kitchen.*)

SUSAN (*quickly*). But if it is still there, then it must belong to Gwenny. Ada, wait——

(ADA *stops above the table and turns to them.* DR. HAGGETT *goes to* SUSAN *and bends over her.*)

DR. HAGGETT (*savagely*). Here we are, at the worst crisis since nineteen-fourteen, with war debts and income tax up to our necks, a fortune in the house, and my own daughter, whom I support, tries to tell me that it belongs to Gwenny ! Has Gwenny got the sense to know what that picture's worth ? (*He turns, paces to below the desk and looks out front.*)

(ADA *goes up to the fireplace.*)

MRS. HAGGETT (*angrily*). I'm surprised at you, Susan, after this morning, when your father was swindled himself !

(DR. HAGGETT *turns and looks at* MRS. HAGGETT *in disgust.*)

ADA. I think it's about time Daddy stuck up for his rights.

(DR. HAGGETT *paces up and down behind the armchair.*)

SUSAN. But that picture is Gwenny's rights !

DR. HAGGETT (*to* SUSAN, *loudly and querulously*). My dear girl, I'm not going to do anything at all that isn't fair and above board. . . . (*Quietly, as he bends over her again.*) And don't talk so loud ! Gwenny might hear.

SUSAN (*rising*). Daddy, I won't stand by and see you take advantage of Gwenny !

(*She flashes out into the hall and upstairs.* DR. HAGGETT *takes several steps after her, as if to stop her.*)

MRS. HAGGETT (*rising and crossing to him*). Don't take any notice of her. There's one thing to do now, and one thing only ! And that is, to find out if Gwenny's planning to take that portrait with her to Manchester.

DR. HAGGETT. Get her down here and ask her.

ADA. She'd guess what you were after.

MRS. HAGGETT. What do you mean, after ?

DR. HAGGETT. Hannah, Ada's right. Not that we've got anything to hide, but she would guess what you were after, all the same.

MRS. HAGGETT. Well, if it was me, I'd just go into her room and take that picture out with me as if it was worth twopence-halfpenny.

(DR. HAGGETT *crosses to the chair at the desk.*)

DR. HAGGETT. Hannah, there is a point of conscience here· Remember the Bible. I must put my thinking-cap on. (*He sits, facing front.*)

MRS. HAGGETT (*following to* R. *of him*). Shut your eyes, Arthur. You always think best with your eyes shut.

(ADA *leans over the back of the chair above the table.*)

(*As he obeys.*) That's right. Now what do we do ?

DR. HAGGETT (*out front, with his eyes shut*). Well, one way of looking at it is, that the portrait is our property. Gwenny isn't what you might call an artist's model, is she ?

MRS. HAGGETT. I should hope not.

DR. HAGGETT. No. Well, that's settled. She's no artist's

model, and she's our servant. We were paying her thirty shillings a month at the time, and her board and lodging. . . .

MRS. HAGGETT. We were only paying her eighteen shillings in those days——

DR. HAGGETT (*opening his eyes*). That doesn't matter; the principle's the same !

MRS. HAGGETT. Yes !

DR. HAGGETT. Now, the question is, had she the right to let him paint it during working hours that I was paying her for out of the sweat of my brow ?

MRS. HAGGETT (*pleased*). Arthur, you're right, your conscience is clear. Without a shadow of a doubt that portrait belongs to us . . . (*She crosses to* L. *of* ADA.) Ada, go upstairs and bring it down.

ADA. But what will Gwenny say ?   (*She goes to the door down* R.)

MRS. HAGGETT (*giving her imagination free rein*). Break the room up ! Tear the window-curtains ! Turn the bed over ! Then your father can say a burglar must have taken it. (*She pushes the chair above the table under the table and crosses to* C.)

DR. HAGGETT (*uncomfortably*). I'm only a simple country doctor. I don't care for money. It's only for the sake of my loved ones that I must have it.

MRS. HAGGETT (*to* DR. HAGGETT). We must get a move on ! (*She turns and crosses above the table to the door* R., *where she pushes* ADA *ahead of her.*) When you've got that picture, you take it down the back staircase. Now hurry up, Ada.

(ADA *goes out.* MRS. HAGGETT *closes the door, then crosses below the table to* L. *of it.*)

Once we've got it, we'll hide it under your bed.

DR. HAGGETT (*to himself*). If Gwenny takes it in the wrong way, I can give her a little something.

(ADA *comes back and closes the door.*)

MRS. HAGGETT. Well ?

ADA. Gwenny's up there.

MRS. HAGGETT. And what about the picture ?

ADA. The picture's there too !

DR. HAGGETT (*rising*). What does it look like ?

ADA. Awful !

DR. HAGGETT. Well, it's some comfort to know it's still all right.

MRS. HAGGETT. What's Gwenny doing ?

ADA. Packing her box.

MRS. HAGGETT. Tell her it's time for her to be getting the dinner ready.

ADA. But if she stays out there in the kitchen . . .

MRS. HAGGETT. Well, tell her it's time to lay the table for dinner.

ADA. Oh, you ask her.

MRS. HAGGETT. Oh, you misery!

(ADA *moves up to the downstage corner of the sideboard.* MRS. HAGGETT *looks at* DR. HAGGETT *for approval. He gestures her to go ahead.*)

(*In her sweetest tones, as she crosses below the table to the door* R.) Gwe-e-e-nny! (*She opens the door.*) Gwe-e-e-nny! (*She closes the door and turns to* DR. HAGGETT.) You must talk to her. (*She moves up to the sideboard, takes out the table-cloth and puts it on the top.*)

(*All three watch the kitchen door.* GWENNY *enters, still in a state of apprehension.*)

DR. HAGGETT (*sitting in the chair at the desk*). Oh, Gwenny. (*With a heroic effort at play-acting.*) I'm sorry I was so short with you just now.

GWENNY (*crossing to below the chair* R. *of the table and eyeing him askance*). Oh, that iss all right, Doctor.

MRS. HAGGETT (*also play-acting*). No, Gwenny, it isn't right, and Doctor Haggett could not rest till he'd asked your pardon.

GWENNY (*eyeing her*). That iss all right, really.

MRS. HAGGETT (*dropping the folded cloth on the table*). And you can go on with your work now, my dear, and lay the table for dinner.

GWENNY. Yes, Mrs. Haggett.

(*She goes above the table and spreads the cloth.* MRS. HAGGETT *nods to* ADA, *who slips into the kitchen.* MRS. HAGGETT *moves over to the kitchen door, closes it and blocks it.*)

DR. HAGGETT (*still acting*). It's really very jolly of you to wait on us on your last day, Gwenny.

GWENNY. It iss nothing, really.

MRS. HAGGETT (*at the door* R.). No, it isn't nothing, Gwenny. And we appreciate it, Doctor Haggett and myself, with the new maid here, too.

GWENNY. It iss nothing. (*She crosses to the sideboard and takes out napkins.*)

DR. HAGGETT. It wouldn't have seemed natural to have the new maid waiting on us at dinner with you still in the house, Gwenny.

GWENNY. No, I suppose it would not have. (*She returns to the table and places the napkins on it.*)

(ADA *returns.*)

ADA (*in a whisper*). Mummy, the new maid's there!

Mrs. Haggett. Tell her to go out and have a walk round the village.

(Ada *turns to the door*.)

And, Ada !

(Ada *turns to her mother*.)

Never mind about the burglar.

(Ada *exits, closing the door*.)

Gwenny (L. *of the table*). Burglar ! What is it about a burglar ?

Mrs. Haggett (*laughing*). Oh, that's only a little joke, Gwenny, you'll hear about it later on.

(Dr. Haggett *laughs*. Gwenny *crosses below the table towards the kitchen*.)

Where are you going, Gwenny ?

Gwenny. I was going into the kitchen to fetch the pickled onions.

Mrs. Haggett (*blocking the door—pleasantly*). Oh, I don't think we need the pickled onions for dinner. Do we, Arthur ?

Dr. Haggett. I'll be straightforward with you, Gwenny. Pickled onions don't seem to agree with me.

Gwenny. Oh, well—— (*She starts again for the kitchen*.)

(Dr. Haggett *rises and moves* o.)

Dr. Haggett. Gwenny !

(Gwenny *turns back again*.)

We don't want any pickled onions.

Gwenny. I wass going to get some pickle jelly. You always have liked my pickle jelly, Doctor.

Mrs. Haggett (*stumped*). She's right, Arthur. You've always had a weakness for her pickle jelly.

Dr. Haggett (*breaking in—likewise stumped*). So I have. And I can't think of a blessed thing against it at the moment. (*He goes up* c.)

Mrs. Haggett (*going up* L., *helpfully*). Weren't you going to say something to Gwenny, Arthur ?

Dr. Haggett (*coming down* c.). Oh—yes—oh—yes.

(Mrs. Haggett *comes down* L.)

Gwenny (*taking a step to him*). What wass it that you wass wanting to say to me, Doctor Haggett ?

Dr. Haggett (*at a total loss*). Oh—one or two things. In the first place—well——

(Ada *returns*.)

ADA (*in a whisper*). Mummy !

MRS. HAGGETT (*crossing* R.). What is it ?

ADA. She says she doesn't want to have a walk.

MRS. HAGGETT. Either she has a walk, or she goes back to Blackpool.

(*She bustles* ADA *out again, and closes the door.*)

GWENNY. Goes back to Blackpool ?

DR. HAGGETT. I know what it was I wanted to talk about, Gwenny. It was about the new maid. What do you think of her ?

GWENNY (*turning to* DR. HAGGETT). Oh, she iss a nice girl.

DR. HAGGETT. Of course she's a nice girl. Mrs. Haggett wouldn't have picked anything else. (*Confidentially.*) But, Gwenny . . . think carefully. Will she give the same satisfaction you have given us ?

GWENNY (*really touched*). Oh, Doctor Haggett ! That iss proper kind of you to say that ! Of course, in fairness, issn't it, you got to remember that I had fifteen years to get used to your manners and your funny ways, like. And I'm not saying that she will be so very sharp as to the way you like your porridge for breakfast, and things like that, without that you tell her. But she iss a nice girl, and if she likes the place, well, good enough——

MRS. HAGGETT. Don't you think she will like it, Gwenny ?

GWENNY. Well, perhaps she will, and perhaps she will not. I will get your dinner first, and talk after. (*Again she starts for the kitchen.*)

(DR. HAGGETT *takes a step after her, helplessly.*)

MRS. HAGGETT (*still blocking the door*). But, Gwenny, you haven't even got the table properly laid yet !

GWENNY (*brushing her aside*). I know, but I cannot stand here jabbering with my rice pudding burning to a cinder.

(*She goes into the kitchen, and closes the door.*)

MRS. HAGGETT. Why didn't you stop her ?

DR. HAGGETT. How could I stop her ? Why didn't you stop her ?

MRS. HAGGETT. Well, you had a good look at me having a try, didn't you ? Now you'll just have to face it. It was cowardly of you to get round her like that.

DR. HAGGETT. It was your idea ! I'd never have done it.

(SUSAN *comes down the stairs and regards them distastefully.*)

MRS. HAGGETT. Shssh ! (*Putting her ear to the kitchen door.*) Listen . . . (*She listens at the door.*)

DR. HAGGETT (*taking a step towards her*). Can you hear anything ?

MRS. HAGGETT. Not a pin dropping !

DR. HAGGETT. Ada must be in her bedroom now! She'll come out with that picture in her hands, and Gwenny . . . Hannah, go out there and do something!

MRS. HAGGETT. I can't! You do something yourself.

(*The telephone rings.* DR. HAGGETT *turns and moves* L. *a step.*)

DR. HAGGETT. I must answer it——

MRS. HAGGETT. You do not! Susan, you answer it.

(SUSAN *goes to the desk to answer the telephone.*)

DR. HAGGETT (*to his wife*). Hannah, call her back in here. I'll have another chat with her.

MRS. HAGGETT. What sort of a chat, for goodness' sake?

SUSAN (*into the telephone*). Hallo!

DR. HAGGETT. Let me think . . . (*He sits on the chair below the table.*) Don't hurry me . . . I'll have a brain-wave, if you wait long enough.

MRS. HAGGETT (*taking a step to him*). We can't wait that long.

SUSAN (*into the telephone*). Yes, Maggie?

MRS. HAGGETT (*to* DR. HAGGETT). You'll take all day.

SUSAN (*into the telephone*). What?

MRS. HAGGETT. Once she catches Ada . . .

DR. HAGGETT (*grasping his wife's arms*). I'll implore her not to leave.

SUSAN (*into the telephone*). What?

DR. HAGGETT. That's what I'll do. I'll plead with her!

MRS. HAGGETT. No, you will not. Because then she mightn't leave, and if she doesn't leave, it'll be twice as hard!

DR. HAGGETT (*breaking in*). Call her, woman! Think of something!

(ADA *returns, tottering. She leaves the door open.*)

MRS. HAGGETT (*starting to call*). Gwe——

(*Her voice catches as she sees* ADA. ADA *crosses to* R. *of* DR. HAGGETT. MRS. HAGGETT *rushes to the door and shuts it.*)

SUSAN (*into the telephone*). Just a minute, Maggie, I'll call him.

MRS. HAGGETT (*to* ADA). Did you get it?

ADA (*gasping, her hand on her heart*). No!

DR. HAGGETT. She didn't nab you?

SUSAN (*calling*). Daddy!

ADA. No. But if the rice pudding hadn't been burning, she'd have nabbed me all right! I was just lifting it off the nail when I looked over my shoulder . . . and there she was, with her head in the oven!

SUSAN (*calling*). Daddy!

(DR. HAGGETT *gestures for* SUSAN *to be quiet.*)

c

MRS. HAGGETT. We'll just have to try again, that's all.

SUSAN (*into the telephone*). Just a minute, Maggie. (*She puts down the telephone receiver and moves* R. *a step.*)

MRS. HAGGETT. We'll eat our dinner quietly, just as if nothing had happened. Then I'll send her out on a message. Come along, Ada. We'll finish laying the table.

(*She turns to the upstage end of the sideboard and begins taking silver out of a drawer.* ADA *goes to lower end and gets a stack of soup-plates.*)

SUSAN. When you've finished with your plotting and your whispering over there, there's a trunk call for Daddy.

MRS. HAGGETT (*turning*). What's that ?

SUSAN. Maggie Frost says it's from London.

MRS. HAGGETT. London !

DR. HAGGETT. London on the telephone !

MRS. HAGGETT. It's that silly Maggie Frost playing a joke. You wait till I get hold of her in Sunday school——

SUSAN. But it is London, Daddy ! I can't get the name. It sounds like Knoedler and Co.

DR. HAGGETT (*very agitated*). I won't talk to any more meddling fools from London. Tell them I'm out ! Tell them I've gone to Nottingham ! Tell them——

(MRS. HAGGETT *crosses to above the table with the silver and cruet.*)

SUSAN. No, Daddy, you tell him your own lies.

(ADA *brings plates and glasses to the table.* MRS. HAGGETT *moves round to* R. *side, then below the table, laying places.*)

DR. HAGGETT. All right, I will. (*He rises, crosses to the desk and sits at the telephone.*) A lot of help you are to your poor old father.

(SUSAN *crosses to above the armchair, her back to the audience.* MRS. HAGGETT *and* ADA *continue to lay the table, straining mechanically to hear every word.*)

Hello . . . Yes. This is Doctor Haggett . . . (*To the others.*) I can hear as plain as anything . . . Who ? . . . What ? . . . " The Grassmere Stone Bridge " ? . . .

(*There is a long pause*)

Speak up, I can't hear.

(*There is another pause.* MRS. HAGGETT *and* ADA *pause and listen intently.*)

How much ?

(Susan *turns to* Dr. Haggett. Mrs. Haggett *is now at the* l. *side of the table,* Ada *at the* r. *side.)*

(After a third pause, dully.) No, I'll think it over. Ring me up to-morrow. *(He rings off, and sits dazed.)*

Mrs. Haggett *(by the chair* l. *of the table, stammering).* What . . . what was it, Arthur ?

Dr. Haggett *(weakly).* He wants to pay me two thousand five hundred guineas for " The Grassmere Stone Bridge " . . . if it's in good condition. *(A desperate echo.)* In good condition ! *(Hysterically.)* Do you hear that, Hannah ? In good condition !

Mrs. Haggett *(leaning on the table, also hysterical).* Two thousand five hundred . . . Two thou . . . !

Ada *(above the table—also hysterical).* That's the one I painted my picture on the back of, and sold for twelve guineas !

Dr. Haggett *(in his swivel chair, shouting).* I know it is !

(Gwenny *comes in from the kitchen carrying a soup tureen.)*

Gwenny. Dinner's ready.

(She *places the tureen at* Mrs. Haggett's *place on the* r. *side of the table. She then moves away to the* r. *a few steps. The* Haggetts *fail to stir.)*

You can all set down. Dinner's ready.

(She eyes them with surprise. Finally, the Haggetts *move mechanically, as though under a spell, towards their respective places at the table.* Mrs. Haggett *goes below the table to her chair on the* r. *side.* Ada *goes to her place below the table.* Susan *sits on the chair above the table, and* Dr. Haggett *sits in the chair* l. *of the table.* Susan *is the only one who unrolls her napkin. Then she and* Ada *both lean forward on the table, staring down dejectedly.* Mrs. Haggett *removes the lid of the tureen and hands it to* Gwenny, *who has taken a position at the table between* Mrs. Haggett *and* Susan. Gwenny *takes the lid to the sideboard and places it there. She then returns to the same position at the table.* Mrs. Haggett *slowly serves the first bowl of soup and hands it to* Gwenny, *who, solicitously, places her other arm about* Susan's *shoulder and bends over to serve her.* Susan, *however, pushes the plate away. Then* Gwenny *hands it to* Dr. Haggett, *who has been following her every move with great concentration. Startled, he takes it very quickly.* Mrs. Haggett *hands the next bowl to* Gwenny, *who goes to* Ada, *who seems unaware of* Gwenny's *presence at her side.* Gwenny, *vexed at the strange behaviour of the* Haggetts, *slaps* Ada *roughly on the shoulder.* Ada *then sits back and* Gwenny *places the bowl before her. However, neither* Dr. Haggett *nor* Ada *touch the soup.* Mrs. Haggett *does not serve herself, but drops her head in her hands in despair.* Gwenny *looks at them queerly, then goes to the sideboard, gets the bread and returns to the table. More mystified*

than ever, she bends over and peers into Mrs. Haggett's *face. Then looks at* Ada *and* Susan. *As she puts the bread on the table, she catches* Dr. Haggett's *eye, who is still watching her.* Gwenny *straightens up indignantly.* Dr. Haggett *quickly lowers his gaze, unrolls his napkin, tucks it in his coat, and bows his head.*)

Dr. Haggett. For what we are about to receive—

(*The* Curtain *starts to fall.*)

—O Lord, make us truly thankful.

(*The* Haggetts *have all lowered their heads, but* Gwenny *continues eyeing them.*)

The Curtain *is down.*

ACT III

The SCENE *is the same. It is about half-past three in the afternoon. Sunshine of less brightness still pours into the room. (See Furniture and Property Plot.)*

At the rise of the CURTAIN, DAVENPORT *is discovered standing at the fireplace, his back to the audience, waiting for* DR. HAGGETT'S *return.* SUSAN *comes downstairs and enters the room.*

SUSAN (*up* C.). How do you do?

DAVENPORT (*turning*). Oh, how do you do?

SUSAN. We haven't met, Mr. Davenport. I'm the other daughter, Susan.

DAVENPORT. Oh, how do you do, Susan?

SUSAN. Mummy told me to beg your pardon for keeping you waiting so long. Daddy went out after dinner, and we don't know where he is, or what's become of him.

DAVENPORT (*crossing to just* R. *of her*). I don't mind waiting. And if your father's errand is what I hope it is, I only trust it may prove successful.

SUSAN (*moving a step nearer to him*). Yes . . . Well, Mr. Davenport, as you seem rather at a loose end at the moment, I—I've got a sort of funny—*favour* to ask you.

DAVENPORT. Please do!

SUSAN (*quickly*). You wouldn't tell my father or mother I asked it, would you?

DAVENPORT (*smiling*). I can keep a secret.

SUSAN. I was thinking of eloping this afternoon.

DAVENPORT. My dear child!

SUSAN. Yes. And you turning up to-day out of the blue is absolutely providential, Mr. Davenport. Because all I need is an art critic.

DAVENPORT (*after a pause*). If you're counting on me to break the news to your parents . . .

SUSAN (*quickly*). Oh, nothing like that!

DAVENPORT. Suppose you explain more fully, then. There's always some reason for an elopement. Either the man's married, or the girl's father and mother don't approve of him.

SUSAN. That's my reason.

DAVENPORT. Why don't they?

SUSAN (*sadly*). Because he's an artist, and they've got no use for artists.

DAVENPORT. Is he a good artist?

SUSAN (*seriously*). He thinks he is, but I'm not a fit judge. So I thought perhaps you'd just hop round and have a look at his pictures, and tell me what you think.

DAVENPORT. I see. Caution the best policy, eh?

SUSAN. What do you mean?

DAVENPORT. Well, I naturally conclude that if his pictures don't come up to expectations, you'll think twice before you marry him?

SUSAN (*with determination*). Oh, I'd marry him whatever happened! I'd marry him if he was the most terrible painter in the world! I just want to know the worst, for my own private information.

DAVENPORT. From one so young, that sounds to me very morbid!

SUSAN. Well, I only want to know whether he ought to paint pictures . . . or houses.

DAVENPORT (*chuckling*). I warn you that if I don't like the pictures——

SUSAN. Don't tell him!

DAVENPORT. Is it wise of you to want to know the truth yourself?

SUSAN. I'll show you I'm not afraid. (*She goes to above the desk and gets the two pictures brought in by* BRUCE *in Act I.*) I've got two of Bruce's pictures here.

(DAVENPORT *moves a step down and* L. *She returns to* L. *of him.*)

They're only little ones, so they don't do him justice. But you can tell me what you think to my face—really you can. (*Extending them for his inspection.*) This one is my dead duck, and this one is my sister's salmon.

(DAVENPORT *takes them, extracts his glasses, and examines first one and then the other.*)

DAVENPORT. Curious! Very curious! (*Turning to her.*) I'd certainly say a pupil of Christopher Bean.

SUSAN (*nodding*). Yes, he was. When he was a little boy. But he's been painting on his own ever since.

DAVENPORT. Oh, they've got their own individuality.

SUSAN. Does that mean they're bad?

DAVENPORT. No, no, it means they make me want to see more of his work. And to meet him. (*He hands the pictures back to her.*)

SUSAN. Oh, that's easy. (*Replacing the pictures above the desk.*) I'll show you where. I'll take you . . . Will you come now? (*She returns to him.*) You see, there isn't much time.

DAVENPORT. At what time is the elopement?

SUSAN. At half-past four, to the minute. So as to catch the Rocklands train with Gwenny.

DAVENPORT. Is Gwenny leaving too ?

(DR. HAGGETT *comes in through the front door. He has his bicycle clips on.*)

SUSAN. Yes, she is. She's going to Manchester, and . . . Shssh ! (*She puts out her hand to warn him.*) Here's Daddy !

(DR. HAGGETT *enters the room, haggard, gives them a look of agony, crosses to the chair* L. *of the table, and sinks wearily into it.*)

Why, Daddy, what's the matter ? Where have you been ?
DR. HAGGETT. All over the blessed place.

(*There is a pause.*)

SUSAN. You look awful.
DR. HAGGETT (*looking at* SUSAN). I feel awful.
DAVENPORT. Oh . . . yes . . . I——
SUSAN. I'm just taking Mr. Davenport out to see the village, Daddy.
DR. HAGGETT. Well, take him, then.
SUSAN (*to* DAVENPORT). You've no objection, Mr. Davenport ?

(*They turn and start for the front door.*)

DAVENPORT. No, your young man should certainly have things to tell me. I must have a talk with Gwenny, too, before she leaves.

(SUSAN *and* DAVENPORT *get their coats and hats from the table in the hall.* MRS. HAGGETT *enters from the kitchen,* R.)

SUSAN (*gaily*). You'll have plenty of time to see Gwenny. . . . It's just across the road.
DAVENPORT. Oh, just across the road, is it ?

(*They go out through the front door, and pass the window.*)

MRS. HAGGETT (*by the chair* R. *of the table*). Well, Arthur ?
DR. HAGGETT. I've been all over the blessed place. Up to the Morston Green cornfield. Down to the Grassmere stone bridge. Up to the cemetery. (*He takes off his bicycle clips.*)
MRS. HAGGETT. What did you go to the cemetery for ?
DR. HAGGETT. To look for that scoundrel who stole " The Grassmere Stone Bridge " from me this morning.
MRS. HAGGETT. Did you think he'd died and buried himself, or something ?
DR. HAGGETT. He's still here. Somewhere. Painting.
MRS. HAGGETT. Painting ?
DR. HAGGETT. I found that out at the " Eccleston Arms." He put his luggage in there this morning, and he hasn't taken it out yet, or paid his bill.
MRS. HAGGETT. Were the pictures in his room ? Why didn't you——

DR. HAGGETT. He took them to the National Provincial Bank. They're in the vault there.

MRS. HAGGETT. Well ?

DR. HAGGETT. The Bank wouldn't let me have them. That silly little fool of a bank manager, Bob Palethorpe, that I was at school with ! . . . And now this robber's gone out again, if you please. He's got his dinner and his painting things with him. His name's Tallant.

MRS. HAGGETT. Tallant . . . two " l's " or one ? (*She moves to above the table.*)

DR. HAGGETT (*looking up at her*). Two. (*Calling.*) Gwenny !

GWENNY (*off* R.). Yes, Doctor !

DR. HAGGETT (*to* MRS. HAGGETT). I've been running my head off all afternoon.

(GWENNY *enters from the kitchen and comes to below the sideboard.*)

(*To* GWENNY). Gwenny, bring me a glass of milk and a dry biscuit.

GWENNY. Wouldn't you fancy something hot, Doctor Haggett ?

DR. HAGGETT. I haven't time to fancy anything hot !

(GWENNY *returns to the kitchen and closes the door.*)

MRS. HAGGETT. There were three more telephone calls. (*She crosses towards the desk.*) And seven more telegrams.

DR. HAGGETT (*testily, as he turns to her with a gesture*). I've got no time for telegrams, either !

(*There is a pause.* MRS. HAGGETT *stops by the lower end of the desk.*)

(*Holding up his trembling hand, pathetically.*) Hannah, look !

(*She turns to him.*)

This sort of thing isn't good for a man of my age ! This morning I was a peaceful country doctor, filled with gentle thoughts of a medical description. Now look ! (*Shaking his hand again.*) If a patient came in with an appendix, I'd miss it by so much I'd put his eye out ! (*Desperately.*) Once you get started on a thing like this, though . . . Once you let it get a hold on you . . .

(*There is a pause. She crosses to the back of him.*)

MRS. HAGGETT (*exasperated*). Oh, keep to the point, Arthur, keep to the point !

DR. HAGGETT. But that's what I am doing ! I remembered Gwenny's leaving on the five-o'clock train, and we can't let her take that portrait with her ! It's the only one we can be sure of laying our hands on.

MRS. HAGGETT. You will have to get to work on her, then. I really can't come to grips with any more to-day.

DR. HAGGETT. That's just what I've come back home to do.

You started it, but I've got to finish it.   I've got everything thought out.   Leave it to me !

(GWENNY *comes in with a glass of milk and a plate of biscuits, and closes the door.   She crosses to above the table and places the glass before* DR. HAGGETT.)

Thank you, Gwenny.   Just what I need.

(MRS. HAGGETT *crosses* L. *to the window.*)

GWENNY.   Now, I have got a nice pork chop, I could hot it up lovely for you——

(*He shudders.*)

DR. HAGGETT (*showing her his hand*).   Gwenny—look !

(MRS. HAGGETT *looks out of the window.*)

GWENNY.   Oh, rannwyl !   I never see you in a state like this before.   It is all them queer London creetchars coming here.

DR. HAGGETT (*with deep self-pity*).   And they're all coming back, Gwenny.   They may be here any minute now !

GWENNY.   Why do you bother your head with them, Doctor Haggett ?

DR. HAGGETT.   One can't shirk one's responsibilities in this life, Gwenny.   (*After a pause, with unaccountable intention.*)   I wouldn't mind so much if this room looked right to me.   It's that awful patch over the fireplace, where Ada's picture was.

(MRS. HAGGETT *crosses to below the armchair.*)

GWENNY (*taking a step up to the fireplace*).   Oh, I will wash off where the smoke hass made a mark off the fire.

DR. HAGGETT.   No.   There's no time to do that.

MRS. HAGGETT.   Couldn't you hang one of that Bruce McRae's pictures there ?   (*She points to the pictures at the upstage end of the desk.*)

DR. HAGGETT.   No !   Bruce's pictures aren't big enough for that. What we want is something to cover up the whole place.   It must be a big picture !

GWENNY.   Oh . . .

(*She starts for the kitchen.   He stops her.   She turns.*)

DR. HAGGETT (*as though struck suddenly by a thought*).   Gwenny, haven't you got a picture Chris Bean painted of you before he died ?

(MRS. HAGGETT *starts.*)

GWENNY.   Oh, yes, I have got my portrait.

DR. HAGGETT.·   Well, if that isn't just the thing, Gwenny !   We'll hang *that* there, over that awful patch !

GWENNY.   Oh, Doctor !

DR. HAGGETT.   Just till you go, Gwenny.

c*

GWENNY. To say the truth, I would like to oblige, sure enough. But, Doctor . . . (*She is covered with embarrassment.*) Dear me, I could not have *my* picture hanging in here. It would not look right.

DR. HAGGETT. Why wouldn't it look right ?

GWENNY. Bobol annwyl, what would people say if they come into your living-room, and see a picture of me hanging up there, ass bold ass brass, scraping carrots !

DR. HAGGETT. What do I care what people'd say ? This is a free country, isn't it ? You've got a vote ? I'd rather have you up there scraping carrots than half these society women that can't scrape anything !

GWENNY. But my portrait hasn't got no frame, even, Doctor Haggett.

DR. HAGGETT. That doesn't matter either. Anything to cover up that awful patch !

MRS. HAGGETT (*crossing to the chair above the table and joining in persuasively*). Don't refuse him, Gwenny, there's a dear.

DR. HAGGETT (*piteously*). Look, Gwenny ! (*He holds up his trembling hand again.*)

GWENNY. Dear me, I never wass able to say " no " to Doctor Haggett.

(*She goes. They catch each other's eye.*)

DR. HAGGETT. A much better way than stealing it would have been. (*He sips his milk.*) This thing's got to be done. But it must be done legitimately. (*He sips his milk.*)

MRS. HAGGETT. But she hasn't given it up to you yet.

DR. HAGGETT. She will. Only you can't take more than one step at a time. I've got it all thought out. Leave it to me. (*He sips his milk.*)

(GWENNY *comes back, carrying the picture. She crosses to the chair* R. *of the table and props the portrait against it. The front of the portrait must not be seen by the audience.*)

GWENNY. Well, here it iss.

DR. HAGGETT (*rising and crossing up stage*). That's really kind of you, Gwenny, upon my soul it is.

GWENNY. It would look better inside a frame.

DR. HAGGETT. There's no time for frames.

MRS. HAGGETT (*to* DR. HAGGETT). What about that picture of your Auntie Mabel on the back landing, it's about the same size, and it's got a lovely frame round it ?

GWENNY. Well, why don't you hang that picture up there, then ?

MRS. HAGGETT. No, no. Auntie Mabel's been dead so long she's happier on the back landing.

(DR. HAGGETT, *after a grateful look at his wife, goes up* C. *to the hall and calls :*)

DR. HAGGETT. Ada!

MRS. HAGGETT. Will you go and get it, Gwenny? (*She moves up stage a little.*)

GWENNY. But I would never want Doctor Haggett to take the frame off his Auntie Mabel!

DR. HAGGETT (*moving down again to* L. *of the table*). I'm very happy to have the opportunity of showing you this little mark of my esteem.

GWENNY (*covered with confusion*). But my picture will look too swanky and dress-up in that frame!

DR. HAGGETT (*with great dignity*). Gwenny, if I put Aunt Mabel's frame round your picture, it isn't for you to say it isn't the right thing.

GWENNY (*apologetically*). I did not mean no offence, Doctor Haggett. I suppose you know best. I will get it.

(*She crosses above table into the hall and goes upstairs.* MRS. HAGGETT *crosses and looks at the portrait.*)

DR. HAGGETT (*to himself*). I said I'd give her something, and I will. I'll give her five pounds.

MRS. HAGGETT (*shaking her head*). You'll never get your money back, Arthur.

DR. HAGGETT (*moving to above the table—crossly*). Hannah, it's hardly for you, that burnt up a fortune, to nag at me for risking five pounds. (*Looking at the portrait.*) I'll be honest with you, though. If it wasn't for those telegrams and telephone calls and what not, I wouldn't be risking fivepence on it.

MRS. HAGGETT (*with great contempt, bending over it*). Look at that awful dab of red on the nose! And the hands are blue!

DR. HAGGETT. Perhaps she's just finished the washing. . . . (*Also bending over the portrait.*) What's she holding?

MRS. HAGGETT. A knife. She *is* scraping carrots.

(GWENNY *comes downstairs, carrying a large, old-fashioned frame, showing front to the audience.*)

GWENNY. Well, whatever, here it iss. Oh, Mrs. Haggett, I feel so silly with it, I do really!

(*She enters and moves to the* L. *side of the table.* DR. HAGGETT *turns and crosses to her.*)

DR. HAGGETT. Put it down just there. Hannah, you clear.

(*He helps* GWENNY *place it face downwards on the table.*)

MRS. HAGGETT (*inaudibly*). I'll just clear away these . . . (*She takes the bowl of flowers and the glass of milk to the sideboard ; then returns to* R. *side of the table.*)

DR. HAGGETT. We'll see if it fits.

(*He lifts the canvas and places it face down in the frame. He uses his*

fist to hammer the canvas into the frame. Both GWENNY *and* MRS.
HAGGETT *crowd about him, aiding him. There is a pause.)*

GWENNY. Doctor, take care not to scratch yourself on those
rusty old nails !

MRS. HAGGETT. Oh, it's too small——

(He quiets her.)

DR. HAGGETT. No, Hannah, it's a little bit tight up there. *(He
bangs the frame.)* That's funny. It was always a bit loose on Aunt
Mabel.

(They finally get the picture fixed firmly in the frame.)

There ! Might have been made for it !

(He picks up the frame and leans it against the upstage L. *side of the
table, on the floor and between the two chairs, its back to the audience.*
MRS. HAGGETT *puts the bowl of flowers back on the table.)*

Now we'll see what it looks like.

(The effect is admired, too warmly by DR. *and* MRS. HAGGETT, *ecstatic-
ally by* GWENNY.)

GWENNY (L. *of* DR. HAGGETT). Oh, whoever would have thought
that my picture could look like that ?

MRS. HAGGETT *(moving to* R. *of* DR. HAGGETT). Wouldn't Chris
Bean be pleased to see it as it is now ?

GWENNY. Oh, dear me, I wish that he could see it !

DR. HAGGETT. It *is* like you, Gwenny. You can't get away from
it.

GWENNY *(proudly).* All the time that he wass painting it, he
wass keeping on at it saying, " Gwenny, this iss my masterpiece that
I am painting at now " !

MRS. HAGGETT *(sharply).* Do you hear that, Arthur ? *(She
nudges his arm.)*

DR. HAGGETT *(sharper).* Gwenny, are you positive he said that ?

GWENNY. Oh, yes, indeed ! And when it was all finished, he
thanked me. He thanked me, Doctor, just ass if I had do something for him . . . *(Her voice breaking.)* Boys like him . . . it
issn't right for boys like him to die so young . . .

MRS. HAGGETT. Now then, Gwenny, you mustn't cry. You'll
have me crying as well. *(She sits on the chair* R. *of the table.)*

DR. HAGGETT *(patting* GWENNY *on the shoulder, and blowing his
nose).* You'll have us all crying. *(He crosses up to the hall and calls.)*
A-da ! Come down here and see Gwenny's portrait. *(He crosses
down to* L. *and below* GWENNY.)

GWENNY *(gratefully).* You are all so good to me . . .

*(*ADA *appears on the stairs, and comes down to* R. *of* GWENNY.)

DR. HAGGETT. We're fond of you, Gwenny. Fonder of you than I can put into words. A simple doctor like me . . . (*Motioning to* ADA.) Look, Ada ! Don't you think that makes a fine effect ?

ADA (*who catches the drift at once*). Oh, yes, rather !

DR. HAGGETT. We've got two Gwennies here now. One in flesh and blood, and the other in oils.

(*They all laugh.*)

It seems a pity to let them both leave us, doesn't it ?

GWENNY. Oh, Doctor Haggett. . . . I do not know how to thank you, indeed I do not . . . And I won't forget, on the Bible, I won't . . .

DR. HAGGETT. . . . Seeing you both like this puts an idea into my head.

MRS. HAGGETT (*seated, swallowing*). I'm sure it's a good one, Arthur.

GWENNY. Oh, Doctor Haggett could not have nothing but good ideas.

DR. HAGGETT. Well, I'll tell it you, just as it came into my head. Since you're leaving us after all these years, Gwenny, it'd be very nice indeed if you left your portrait behind, here with us.

(ADA *goes to above* MRS. HAGGETT.)

GWENNY (*unable to grasp this*). Leave it here for good ? Do you mean for me to go away without it ?

DR. HAGGETT (*explaining quickly*). Oh, I wouldn't ask you to make a sacrifice like that without giving you something instead of it.

GWENNY (*incredulous*). But what could you give to me instead of it ?

DR. HAGGETT (*on the spot again*). Oh, I don't say I could give you anything to make up for what the portrait would mean to *us*. But I have an idea, Gwenny, that five pounds would come in pretty useful in Manchester.

(GWENNY *shakes her head.*)

ADA. Make it ten, Daddy.

(MRS. HAGGETT *reaches out and grasps* ADA'S *arm.* DR. HAGGETT *looks at* ADA.)

DR. HAGGETT. All right, I will. I will make it ten pounds. Upon my soul, I will. It's a bit of a squeeze handing out presents that size, in these days, but I will make it ten pounds. I don't think Gwenny'll have much to say against that !

GWENNY (*embarrassed*). No, Doctor Haggett. I have not got anything to say against it. It is a wonderful pressant, like——

DR. HAGGETT (*to* MRS. HAGGETT). There you are ! All settled !

MRS. HAGGETT. Arthur, you're wonderful !

DR. HAGGETT (*no relief like a guilty conscience put to rest*). All square and above-board.

GWENNY. But I could never see my way to giving up my portrait.

(ADA *reacts to this. There is a pause.*)

DR. HAGGETT. Gwenny, you astound me.

GWENNY. Well, Doctor Haggett, I am funny about things that I have had got so long as that.

DR. HAGGETT (*gravely paternal*). You'd better think twice, Gwenny, before you refuse what I'm bound to say is a generous offer.

ADA (*quickly*). How'd it be, Gwenny, if we had a nice photo taken of it, and gave it you to have with you in Manchester ?

MRS. HAGGETT (*delighted*). Now really, Arthur, isn't that a bright idea of our little Ada's ? I must say I'd never have thought of that myself !

GWENNY (*distracted, breaking in*). You have got me so upset that I do not know what to do, really ! I had no idear that you wass all so fond of me !

MRS. HAGGETT. Gwenny !

GWENNY. No, indeed I had not, Mrs. Haggett ! I knowed that Susan wass, but I had no idear about you and Ada and the Doctor. And it iss so very hard for me to say no, only . . .

DR. HAGGETT (*so warmly*). Then don't say no, Gwenny. Say yes, and let's shake hands on it.

GWENNY. Oh ! . . . (*After a slight pause.*) I know what I will do—I will get the photo for you, Mrs. Haggett. I will get it made in Manchester and send it back to Childer Barnston.

DR. HAGGETT (*controlling his impatience*). But don't you see, Gwenny, it's the——

ADA. It's the colour and everything 'that makes it so much—— *(Simultaneously.)*

MRS. HAGGETT. No photo would ever give us the comforting feeling that we had you still with us, Gwenny.

GWENNY. Goodness me, would it really mean so very much to you to have me hanging up there in a oil painting ?

MRS. HAGGETT. Would we want anybody we didn't love, hanging up in our house ?

GWENNY. But I have got so used to looking at that portrait.

DR. HAGGETT (*reproachfully*). But, Gwenny, that's no better than if you sat down all day in front of a looking-glass !

GWENNY. But it issn't me that I see in the picture ! . . . It . . . it iss the time when I wass young ! It iss how things used to be, in the old days, and everything ! It . . . it is . . . but I cannot say it. . . . Well, if you are all made up your minds.

(*The front-door bell rings.*)

MRS. HAGGETT (*inaudibly*). There's somebody at the door.

ADA (*taking a step to* L.). Don't disappoint us, Gwenny.

DR. HAGGETT. She won't disappoint us. You know you won't, Gwenny. You'll say yes, eh ? Think of it. Ten pounds.

(*The front-door bell rings again.*)

GWENNY. Well, if you are all made up your minds that you want——

MRS. HAGGETT (*smiling—to her husband*). Now our own dear Gwenny is speaking at last.

GWENNY (*to* MRS. HAGGETT). No. I have still got to think.

(*There is a movement from* MRS. HAGGETT *and* ADA. *The front door opens.* TALLANT *enters, a painting dangling carefully from his right hand.*)

DR. HAGGETT (*silencing the two women with a gesture*). Of course you've got to think, Gwenny ! And I want you to think, and I know you won't come to any wrong conclusion. You go and sit down on your bed for ten minutes.

(*There is a general gasp from the three* HAGGETTS *as they see* TALLANT.)

TALLANT (*as he enters the room*). Nobody answered the door, so I took the liberty of—— (*He puts the picture against the medical cabinet, its back to the audience, and his hat on the cabinet.*)

GWENNY (*crossing to his* R.). If you have come for my portrait, I cannot let you have it.

(TALLANT *looks at the portrait.*)

I made up my mind that I could not let you have it, anyway, and now it seems I have got to make other arrangements. (*Crossing above the table to the kitchen door.*) So if you will excuse me, Mistar Brown.

(*She exits and closes the door.*)

ADA (*up* R.C.). Were you after Gwenny's portrait, as well as what you've got ?

MRS. HAGGETT (L.C., *breaking in quickly*). You said you were Davenport. She called you Brown. Who in Heaven's name are you ?

DR. HAGGETT (*breaking in*). I didn't expect you to come here of your own free will, Mr. Tallant.

TALLANT (*taking a step down to* DR. HAGGETT). Would you ask the ladies to leave us alone together ?

MRS. HAGGETT (*quickly*). Have you got secrets ?

TALLANT (*to her*). Of the most delicate nature. (*He returns to his scrutiny of the portrait.*)

DR. HAGGETT (*to* MRS. HAGGETT). That's all right, Hannah, leave him to me. (*He points to* TALLANT, *then turns and crosses down to the desk.*)

ADA (*crossing to the hall up* C.). You watch out, Daddy! If he tries to get that one too, shoot him!

MRS. HAGGETT (*rising, and crossing above the table to behind* ADA). If you want any help, Arthur, call me. (*At* TALLANT.) I shall be listening.

TALLANT (*moving up to her*). Yes, I'm sure you will! But your husband and I are going to be great friends, now.

(*He bows them out into the hall.* ADA *and* MRS. HAGGETT *go upstairs. He closes the door.*)

DR. HÅGGETT (*crossing up to* TALLANT). I don't attach much importance to that last remark of yours, Mr. Tallant. You as good as stole a mountain of money from me this morning.

TALLANT (*looking at the picture*). I must ask you to be a little more careful with your language, Doctor Haggett.

DR. HAGGETT. What's your opinion of the mean trick that you played on me?

TALLANT (*still looking at the picture*). It was a simple business operation, carried through in the classic tradition of art collecting.

(*There is reaction from* DR. HAGGETT.)

Not a day passes but some collector finds some rare and unappreciated work of art.

DR. HAGGETT. Did you even know Chris Bean?

TALLANT (*smiling, and turning to look at him*). Never heard of him till a month ago.

DR. HAGGETT. God, you have got a nerve!

TALLANT (*taking a step down to* DR. HAGGETT). Quite! But to come down to business, how much have you told Davenport about the pictures Bean left here?

DR. HAGGETT. I didn't tell him anything. I was still hoping to find the others.

TALLANT. You haven't succeeded?

DR. HAGGETT (*with a groan*). No. They've been burnt. All but the two you've got, and that one there.

(*He indicates the portrait.* TALLANT *goes and looks at it.*)

TALLANT (*admiringly*). Yes, a masterpiece!

DR. HAGGETT (*dryly*). I'm glad you like it.

TALLANT. Oh, you and I can hardly hope to reach that height.

DR. HAGGETT. You and I? What are you blithering about?

TALLANT (*returning to* L. *of* DR. HAGGETT). Corot . . .

(*As* DR. HAGGETT *does not see light.*)

The name means nothing to you?

DR. HAGGETT. Not a thing.

TALLANT. No! Corot was a French painter of landscapes. He

died in eighteen-seventy-five. The bulk of his painting has been done since then.

(DR. HAGGETT *is startled.*)

Well, the same is true of the late Cézanne. He died in nineteen hundred and six. I know a dozen excellent Cézannes, all painted during the last year. (*He turns up and gets the picture he brought in with him.*) I spoke this morning of a business partnership between us. Allow me! . . . (*Exhibiting it.*) "The Briar Turnpike Cornfield" by the late Christopher Bean.

(DR. HAGGETT *starts to take it from him.*)

Be careful! Don't touch it! It's not dry yet!

DR. HAGGETT (*drawing back*). Where did you find it?

TALLANT. I painted it.

(*There is a pause.*)

DR. HAGGETT. What are you?

TALLANT. A forger.

(*He drops the picture to his side. Light dawns on* DR. HAGGETT.)

I see that you begin to understand. Those letters in the "London Mercury" tell us about the pictures that Bean left here. The originals are lost. Thanks to *my* peculiar gifts, their loss needn't disturb us. (*As* DR. HAGGETT *gasps.*) I assure you, Doctor Haggett, I am offering you a gold-mine. We have an absolute corner in Christopher Beans.

DR. HAGGETT (*looking at him*). Corner?

TALLANT. Well, monopoly. For you can not only vouch for my forgeries, but can also discredit my competitors. Have I made myself clear?

(*He turns and places his painting against the medical cabinet again, its back to the audience. Then he returns to* DR. HAGGETT. *There is a pause.* DR. HAGGETT *mops his brow.*)

DR. HAGGETT. It isn't right! (*After a pause.*) It's criminal! (*He turns and goes to the desk-chair.*)

TALLANT. Not at all. (*He follows to* R. *of* DR. HAGGETT.)

DR. HAGGETT (*sitting*). It's too risky!

TALLANT. Perhaps, but no picture-collecting simpleton ever admits he's been taken in, so . . .

DR. HAGGETT. I don't like the sound of it at all. I was all right this morning, before you came in! I was respected by the world, and at peace with myself. I was tempted by nothing and by no man!

TALLANT. As I remarked this morning, we are all mortal, Doctor. You have a wife and two lovely daughters . . .

DR. HAGGETT (*brightening*). Yes, you're right there. And being tempted for one's loved ones is not half so bad as being tempted on your own account. . . . (*After an uneasy glance towards the portrait.*) How much would I get from this . . . scheme of yours ?

TALLANT. I thought twenty per cent.

DR. HAGGETT. Not worth it.

TALLANT. I'll be liberal. Twenty-five.

DR. HAGGETT. Not a farthing under fifty !

TALLANT (*drawing himself up*). If you persist in letting your greed come between you and . . .

DR. HAGGETT (*rising*). My greed ! Mine ! (*After a pause, knowingly.*) You can't work this scheme without my help. Because I'm in a position to discredit you !

TALLANT (*smiling, holding out his hand*). Doctor Haggett, it's done !

(*Then* DR. HAGGETT *realizes. It is hard for him to take the hand, but he manages to do it. Voices are audible in the hall.*)

MRS. HAGGETT (*in the hall*). I suppose you'd better go in. . . .

(ROSEN *opens the door and enters the room to* L. *of the table, stopping astonished at sight of* TALLANT.)

DR. HAGGETT (*shaking* TALLANT'S *hand*). I'd better warn Mrs. Haggett and Ada that they'd better not talk. . . .

ROSEN (*to* TALLANT). You up here too ?

TALLANT (*his smile fading as he turns to* ROSEN). I got here first, Rosen.

ROSEN. So it was you who . . . Well, I might have known it !

DR. HAGGETT. Are you two acquainted with each other ?

TALLANT. Mr. Rosen will be the selling end of our firm.

DR. HAGGETT (*to* MRS. HAGGETT *and* ADA, *who are visible in the hall*). Hannah, clear out of here and shut that door.

(MRS. HAGGETT *closes the hall door.*)

TALLANT. We have just formed our limited company, as it were, Rosen. Are you coming in on the ground floor ?

ROSEN. I'm not talking your sort of business to-day, thanks. I've come up here after the real thing, and I'm going to get it !

TALLANT (*indicating* GWENNY'S *portrait*). There it is, if you can pay the price for it.

ROSEN (*going to the portrait*). Aha ! . . . (*Bending to examine it.*) It isn't signed.

TALLANT (*laughing*). That's easily seen to.

ROSEN. Oh, one of yours, is it ?

TALLANT (*winking at* DR. HAGGETT). Thanks.

DR. HAGGETT. It's nothing of the kind ! It's——

TALLANT (*turning to* DR. HAGGETT). It's all right, Doctor. He isn't one of the picture-collecting simpletons. I forge most of the pictures he sells.

ROSEN. I know you're good, Tallant, but I never knew you were as good as this!

TALLANT (*delighted, crossing to below the table*). You recognize my brushwork, then?

ROSEN (*laughing*). You can't fool me. (*To* DR. HAGGETT.) If it was real, I'd buy it, but . . . (*He moves down to* C.)

DR. HAGGETT. It is real!

ROSEN (*pointing to* TALLANT). With him on the premises?

TALLANT. Word of honour!

ROSEN (*to* TALLANT). Yours?

DR. HAGGETT. Mine!

ROSEN. Oh!

TALLANT. There you are! . . . (*As* ROSEN *looks at it.*) We'll take four thousand for it.

(DR. HAGGETT *gasps.* ROSEN *moves down a step.*)

ROSEN (*amused*). Now isn't that good of you! Would you consider throwing in the frame?

(DAVENPORT *and* SUSAN *pass the window.*)

TALLANT. Within a year you'll get twice that for it.

ROSEN. If it was genuine I might.

DR. HAGGETT. But it is genuine, on my word of honour as a churchwarden! My only trouble is that I'm not in a position to . . .

ROSEN. I hope you'll excuse me doubting your word, Doctor Haggett, but . . . (*He indicates* TALLANT.)

(TALLANT *takes a step to* ROSEN.)

TALLANT (*breaking in, quickly*). Come on, now, Rosen! Admit you don't know!

(ROSEN *goes back to the portrait and looks at it.* TALLANT *laughs at him.* DR. HAGGETT *goes up* L.C.)

ROSEN (*exploding*). Well! Which is it, genuine or not?

(*The* L. *double hall door is opened and* DAVENPORT *appears. He is speaking to* SUSAN, *who has come back with him and is on her way upstairs.*)

TALLANT (*indicating* DAVENPORT). Here comes Davenport. Ask him!

(ROSEN, R.C., *has his back to* DAVENPORT. TALLANT *moves* R. *a few steps.*)

DAVENPORT (*up* C.). Well, Doctor Haggett, have you found the missing treasures?

(DR. HAGGETT *gestures to the portrait.* DAVENPORT *sees the portrait.*)

Ah! (*To* ROSEN, *who is in front of the portrait.*) Allow me, Rosen.

Rosen. Certainly. (*He moves aside to* R.)

Davenport (*after a pause*). And the man who painted this died miserably ! Here is all womanhood. Its nobility . . . (*Dropping down to one knee.*) Its tenderness and its strength. This is beautiful as only . . . as only . . . (*Rising.*) Damn comparisons ! The thing's beautiful ! (*He backs up stage a step.*)

Rosen. That's all I need to hear. Doctor Haggett, I'll give fourteen hundred guineas for it.

(Mrs. Haggett *comes in from the hall to above the armchair.* Dr. Haggett *drops into the armchair.*)

Davenport. You're not buying it, Rosen !

Rosen. Yes, I am, Mr. Davenport, and I'm jolly glad to have you here to see me do it !

Davenport. What do you want with it ?

(Ada *enters from the hall and stands* L. *of the medical cabinet.*)

Rosen (*to* Davenport, *exultantly*). To show it in my gallery ! A one-man show ! A one-picture show ! For a whole month before I even try to sell it. I'm going to bring all Duveen's clientele down to the Fulham Road !

Davenport (*with a laugh*). Are you going to force me to respect you at last ?

Rosen. Yes, I am. Even if it ruins me ! (*He crosses above the table to the chair* R. *and sits.*) Come on, now, Doctor ! Be reasonable, and we'll talk business.

(Susan *comes down the stairs and enters the room to* L. *of* Ada. *The positions now are :* Rosen *seated on the chair* R. *of the table ;* Tallant *up* R. ; Davenport *upstage by the* L. *end of the mantelpiece ;* Ada L. *of the medical cabinet ;* Susan *up* C. ; Mrs. Haggett *behind, and just to the* L. *of the armchair* L.C. ; Dr. Haggett *seated in the armchair* L.C.)

Dr. Haggett (*utterly distracted*). I—I—I . . . I'd like to sell it . . . but . . . You see, I'm not in a position . . .

Susan (*taking a step towards the armchair*). Don't you do anything you'd be ashamed of, Daddy !

(Mrs. Haggett *and* Ada *grasp* Susan's *arm and push her aside.*)

Dr. Haggett. You clear out of here, my girl ! I won't have any child of mine criticizing me !

Davenport. Doctor Haggett, please !

Dr. Haggett. I can't talk business with women cluttering up the place !

Mrs. Haggett. Arthur !

Rosen. Seventeen hundred guineas.

Dr. Haggett. I tell you I'm not in a position to sell this, yet.

MRS. HAGGETT (*taking a step down and bending over him on his* L.). You'd better hurry up. Don't forget her train leaves Rocklands at five.

DR. HAGGETT. I know it does! Where *is* Gwenny?

MRS. HAGGETT (*pointing to the door* R.). In the kitchen.

DR. HAGGETT (*changing his mind—rising*). No, never mind. (*To* TALLANT, *as he crosses to the chair* L. *of the table.*) Might as well be hanged for a sheep as a lamb.

TALLANT (*moving to the table, above* ROSEN). Leave this to me, partner. I'll handle it.

DR. HAGGETT. You shut up as well, this part of the business doesn't concern you.

(*He glances nervously towards the kitchen door, then turns to* ROSEN *and goes off the deep end.* TALLANT *goes up to below the fireplace.*)

Seventeen hundred guineas . . . is *not* enough! (*He sits down heavily, on the chair* L. *of the table.*)

ROSEN. Don't be foolish!

DR. HAGGETT. It is not enough!

ROSEN. You've got to think of my expenses.

DR. HAGGETT. I don't care a pin for your expenses! Seventeen hundred guineas is not——

ROSEN. How do I know I'll ever be able to sell it?

DR. HAGGETT. I don't know that I'm so very anxious to sell.

ADA (*in the doorway*). Daddy!

MRS. HAGGETT (*crossing to* L. *of him*). Don't forget you risked ten pounds on it!

DR. HAGGETT. I haven't risked it yet!

(MRS. HAGGETT *takes a step down, to watch the kitchen door.*)

ROSEN. Two thousand guineas, then, and that's the limit!

DR. HAGGETT. No!

ROSEN. How much do you want?

DR. HAGGETT (*after another anxious glance towards the kitchen door*). Well, I'm not quite ready to sell this, yet . . . but if I do, you've got to make it worth my while. (*With a gulp.*) I would take seven thousand guineas!

(*There is a gasp from the* HAGGETT *ladies.*)

ROSEN (*laughing*). You're off your head.

(DAVENPORT *moves down to above the table.*)

DR. HAGGETT. Six thousand five hundred!

ROSEN. Even that, Mr. Davenport . . .

DAVENPORT. A little high.

DR. HAGGETT. Six thousand!

MRS. HAGGETT (*standing behind him*). Don't slip, now, Arthur, don't slip!

DR. HAGGETT (*to her*). I have no intention of slipping. (*After another nervous glance towards the kitchen door, to* ROSEN.) And you've got to be sharp about it.

ROSEN. Two thousand five hundred!

DR. HAGGETT
MRS. HAGGETT } (*together*). No!
ADA

ROSEN. Three thousand!

DR. HAGGETT
MRS. HAGGETT } (*together*). *No!!*
ADA

DAVENPORT (*to* ROSEN). You're dealing with a united family, Rosen.

SUSAN (*taking a step to* DAVENPORT). Not with me, Mr. Davenport. And I want to tell you I won't have anything to do with it.

DR. HAGGETT (*beside himself*). Go up to your bedroom, girl! You'll get what's coming to you, poking your fingers into business that's right outside your scope!

SUSAN. I don't care. I just can't bear to see Gwenny—Gwenny——

(*She runs upstairs, indignantly.*)

ADA (*looking at* SUSAN, *then turning to* DAVENPORT, *covering her exit quickly*). My sister isn't quite right in the head. She fell on it when she was a baby.

MRS. HAGGETT (*crossing up to* L. *of* ADA). She's a silly, foolish girl, that's all she is! (*Pushing* ADA *before her towards the kitchen.*) She can't bear to part with the picture, having had it in the house so long.

DR. HAGGETT. I can part with it, though! (*Looking at his watch.*) Damnation!

MRS. HAGGETT (*in a whisper, to* ADA). Keep Gwenny out of here.

(ADA *goes into the kitchen and closes the door.* MRS. HAGGETT *turns and watches* DR. HAGGETT.)

DR. HAGGETT. Six thousand guineas, Mr. Rosen! Take it or leave it.

ROSEN. Well, I certainly won't take it!

DAVENPORT (*to* ROSEN). You've met your match this time, Rosen!

ROSEN. Three thousand five hundred!

DR. HAGGETT. Six thousand!

ROSEN. Cash in three days!

DR. HAGGETT. Five thousand seven hundred!

MRS. HAGGETT (*quickly, as she totters a step* L.). Don't let go, Arthur, don't let go!

ROSEN. Four thousand three hundred! Half of it down, and the balance to-morrow!

Dr. Haggett. Four thousand seven hundred, on the same terms !

(There is a slight pause.)

Rosen *(pounding the table with his fist)*. Done !
Davenport *(above the table)*. Good work, Rosen.
Dr. Haggett *(on the verge of collapse, but still painfully conscious of that kitchen door)*. Let's see the money !
Rosen *(truculently)*. Good God, give me time . . . *(He takes his cheque book, pen and bills of sale out of his coat pocket.)*

(Ada returns, and closes the door.)

Ada. Mummy——
Mrs. Haggett. What is it ?
Ada. The new maid from Blackpool——
Mrs. Haggett. What about her ?
Ada. She's going *back* to Blackpool.
Mrs. Haggett *(smiling)*. Let her go !

(The front-door bell rings.)

Hulloa, there's someone at the door. Will you answer it, and if it's a patient, tell them your father's retired.

(Ada goes above the table and out to answer the door.)

Rosen *(breaking in)*. I had that bill of sale with me for two hundred pounds. *(Looking at his cheque book.)* Now I'll just have to change the figure.

(He writes. Dr. Haggett watches him fascinated. Ada admits Bruce McRae.)

Ada *(to Bruce, at the door)*. What are you doing here, Bruce ?

(Bruce enters to L. side of the C. door. Ada closes the front door and enters to R. side of the door.)

Bruce. I've come for Gwenny's box.
Davenport *(moving a few steps L.)*. Ah, the boy marvel !
Mrs. Haggett. Who ? Bruce McRae ?
Bruce. Hello, Mr. Davenport.
Davenport. I've been looking at his pictures, Mrs. Haggett. You produce talented painters in this village.
Mrs. Haggett *(incredulous, down R.)*. Are his pictures good too ? *(She crosses up to the hall and calls.)* Susan ! Bruce is here ! *(She returns to R. of Bruce.)* Come in, my dear, come in ! Don't be afraid ! We've changed our minds about artists since this morning.

(Ada glares at Bruce.)

BRUCE (*still truculent*). Aye ? Well, I think, if ye don't mind, I'll just get that box.

(*He goes out* C. *and along the passage to* R. SUSAN *has hurried downstairs and follows him off.*)

ROSEN (*to* DR. HAGGETT). Now, you sign here. (*He hands his pen and bill of sale papers to* DR. HAGGETT, *who glances towards the kitchen door and signs.*) And here's the cheque. (*He hands over the cheque.*)

(MRS. HAGGETT *crosses down to* L. *of* DR. HAGGETT.)

DR. HAGGETT. How do I know I get the balance to-morrow ?

(MRS. HAGGETT *crosses to the kitchen door and listens.*)

ROSEN. My God, it's in writing, isn't it ?

DR. HAGGETT. Well, so long as you get that picture out of this house before—— (*He gives another uneasy glance towards the kitchen door.*)

ROSEN (*rising and crossing above the table to the portrait*). That's just what I'm going to do. (*He starts removing the portrait from its frame.*)

DR. HAGGETT (*rising*). Hannah, watch that door !

MRS. HAGGETT (*inaudibly*). Look out, Arthur !

(*She crosses quickly to* L. *of the table.* GWENNY *enters, dressed for her departure, and carrying a suitcase.* MRS. HAGGETT *gasps with dismay.* DR. HAGGETT *goes to* L. *of* GWENNY.)

GWENNY. I'm sorry to break in on you, Doctor Haggett, but my train goes at five o'clock. (*Putting down the suitcase below the sideboard.*) And I have make my mind up . . .

DR. HAGGETT (*breaking in*). I knew it was all right, Gwenny ! I knew it was ! (*Fumbling notes out of his pocket.*) And here is the ten pounds I promised you. (*He forces the money into her hand.*) God bless you, Gwenny ! (*He is hurrying her towards the kitchen door.*)

GWENNY (*wrenching herself free from him*). What iss that man doing there with my portrait ?

ROSEN (*blandly*). Taking it to London, Gwenny ! To exhibit it !

(*She crosses slowly below the table to* L. *of it.*)

Where everybody'll come and look at it ! Could you let me have some brown paper and string ?

GWENNY. What right have you got to take it away ?

ROSEN. Well, I never paid more for a right in my life !

GWENNY (*flatly*). It belong to me.

(*There is a sensation, then a pause.*)

Rosen. How's that ?

(Tallant *smirks*.)

Gwenny. It belong to me.

Dr. Haggett (R. *of her*). What do you want in here, Gwenny ? Who asked you to come in here, anyway ?

Gwenny. I come in to say good-bye, and fetch my portrait, and I have just see him sneaking himself to try and go off with it.

Dr. Haggett (R. *of her*). But you just sold it to me !

Gwenny. Oh, I never did ! I never did !

Mrs. Haggett (L.C.). You've got the money there in your hand, Gwenny.

Davenport (*above the table*). Doctor Haggett ! It can't be that you . . .

Gwenny (*violently*). Here ! Take this money back ! Go on, take it back !

(*He takes it.*)

You tell me that you wass wanting my portrait for to remember me with ! I say to you that I would think about the giving it to you ! And I have think ! And I am not going to part with it, never ! never ! And now you are trying to sell it behind my face ! I would be ashame' as never was, ashame' !

(Dr. Haggett *lowers his head. The positions are now :* Tallant *up* R. *;* Davenport *up stage by* L. *of fireplace ;* Ada *up stage by the medical cabinet ;* Dr. Haggett *just* L. *of the portrait ;* Gwenny *and* Rosen *are* C., Gwenny R. *of* Rosen *;* Mrs. Haggett L.C.)

Mrs. Haggett. Gwenny !

Gwenny. The old-fashion sly trick !

Dr. Haggett (*breaking in explosively*). This is my house, Gwenny Thomas, and everything in it belongs to me, and you are my servant, paid with my wages.

Davenport (*indignantly*). Good God !

Gwenny (*fortissimo*). This portrait iss not belong to you !

Dr. Haggett (*desperately*). If you would all step into the passage, Mr. Davenport, and leave me to clear matters up with Gwenny ! There'll be no more difficulty. . . . Just five minutes, Hannah !

(*There are general murmurs as he and* Mrs. Haggett *urge the company out.*)

Rosen (*protesting*). Damn it, Doctor, I just gave you a cheque for——

Dr. Haggett. Now don't get upset, Mr. Rosen, please. There's a little misunderstanding here, that's all.

(*He closes the door on them all, mops his brow and turns to* Gwenny. *She places the portrait against the chair* L. *of the table.*)

Gwenny, you're not very grateful, after all we've done for you. (*He crosses down to* L. *of her.*)

GWENNY (*at bay—in a low voice*). I cannot help that, Doctor, I will not part with my portrait.

DR. HAGGETT. And I was just working up a lovely surprise for you.

GWENNY. Yes, I catch you at it! And I would be proper ashame'!

DR. HAGGETT. Do you think I was doing something underhand, Gwenny?

GWENNY. Underhand, sneaky and greedy! I always know that Mrs. Haggett and Ada wass greedy, the both of them; but I never know that you wass!

DR. HAGGETT (*hurt*). Gwenny, how can you say that about me! When I was only trying to make a little money for you! Oh, I don't mean that ten pounds. That was only a joke. I was really going to give you two hundred pounds. Think of it, Gwenny. Two hundred pounds!

GWENNY. And you wass going to get two hundred pounds with selling my portrait?

DR. HAGGETT. People in your position, Gwenny, shouldn't own things that are worth so much money.

GWENNY. Perhaps you are right, I do not know . . . but my portrait iss all that I got in the world . . . The boy that painted it . . . Well, I am not ashame' to say it now, it iss so long ago. Then I love him, and I still love him. And he died just after he finish painting it, so it wass the last thing that he ever paint. . . . That iss why it mean that much to me. . . . It means all the happiness that I ever had. And you know I have not had that much, Doctor Haggett. . . . And now, I think I better go and catch my train. (*She moves down to below the table.*)

(*He follows and grasps her arm. She stops.*)

DR. HAGGETT. Gwenny, you're only thinking of yourself. How about your brother and his children? He's a poor man, Gwenny.

GWENNY. I know that he iss . . .

DR. HAGGETT. And he's out of work now.

GWENNY. I know that he iss . . .

DR. HAGGETT. You'll all be hard up over in Manchester.

GWENNY. I cannot help it, Doctor, I cannot really!

DR. HAGGETT. And his children. Wouldn't you like *them* to have advantages, Gwenny?

GWENNY (*breaking in*). But I promise Chris Bean faithful that I would never part with it. The last time I ever see him, I promise that. He paint it for me.

DR. HAGGETT. Who's greedy now? Who would your brother's children say was greedy?

GWENNY. Do not nag at me! Let me go and catch my train.

Dr. Haggett (*after a gulp, his tone changing*). Gwenny, there's something else that you haven't thought of. The portrait doesn't even belong to you.

(*She gasps. He drives on.*)

It was time I paid for, that you wasted sitting down for Chris Bean to paint it, when you should have been working.

Gwenny (*indignantly*). That issn't true. I wass working every minute of the time he was painting. Every minute. I can see us now out in that shed, with me working and him painting.

Dr. Haggett. It was our tea you used to take him out for him to drink.

Gwenny. I never did! You know how Mrs. Haggett was always watching the tea. That wass my own tea, from my own breakfast, that I save for him, and take out to him. Dennachi! What other mischief are you going to try on?

Dr. Haggett. Gwenny, I'll be honest with you. . . . They want to pay me four thousand seven hundred guineas for your portrait.

Gwenny (*stunned*). Four thou——

Dr. Haggett. Divide with me, Gwenny. (*Poignantly.*) You take half, and give me half. If it wasn't for me, you wouldn't be having any of it.

Gwenny (*decisively*). No, I will not!

Dr. Haggett. Take more than half! Take three thousand! Think what you could do for your brother's children with three thousand.

Gwenny (*backing*). No! No, I tell you, no!

Dr. Haggett (*grasping her arm*). Take three thousand five hundred.

Gwenny. Let loose of my dress!

Dr. Haggett. Greed, Gwenny, greed!

Gwenny (*fortissimo*). It iss not greed! I would not take a million pounds. You ought to be ashame'!

(*There is a pause.*)

Dr. Haggett (*with a despairing gesture*). I am. (*He turns, crosses to the armchair and sits.*)

(*There is a long pause.*)

Gwenny (*following to* R. *of him*). Well, now will you leave me to go?

Dr. Haggett. Yes, Gwenny. I'll have to leave you to go now.

(Gwenny *looks lovingly at the portrait, then a thought strikes her.*)

Gwenny. He wass that poor, wass Chris . . . He never had no good coat, nor nothing warm, only that one sweater that I knit for him. He never had no warm room for sleeping in the night, he

never had nothing that he wass needing. He wass that poor . . .
If he could have had the money to go to that warm foreign place,
he need not have die. In the winter, I used to pray for the frost
to go off quick, for Chris's sake. How iss it that a man can die so
poor, when he paint pictures that iss worth so much ? . . .

DR. HAGGETT. Because nobody wanted his pictures when he
was alive, Gwenny.

GWENNY. But I always like them. That iss why I keep so
many. (*She crosses below the table to the suitcase.*)

(DR. HAGGETT *has turned slowly.*)

Not just because he paint them.

DR. HAGGETT. You . . . kept so many ?

GWENNY (*below the table, turning to him*). Yes. I kept them.

DR. HAGGETT (*wetting his dry lips, feverishly*). How did you get
them ?

GWENNY. Mrs. Haggett put them in the bonfire, and I take
them off.

DR. HAGGETT. Where are they now ? (*He rises.*)

GWENNY. In my box. I roll them up. But they are all right.
(*She starts again for her suitcase.*)

DR. HAGGETT (*all but voiceless*). How many are there ?

GWENNY (*stopping again*). There iss seventeen.

DR. HAGGETT (*with a gasp*). Seventeen, Gwenny ? Did you
say . . . seventeen ? (*He turns, and runs up to the hall door,
shouting.*) Hannah ! Ada ! Rosen !

(MRS. HAGGETT *runs in.*)

MRS. HAGGETT. Good heavens, Arthur, what's the matter ?

(ADA *runs in to up* c.)

ADA. Daddy !

(ROSEN *runs in to* L. *of the table, followed by* TALLANT *to above*
DR. HAGGETT, *and* DAVENPORT *to above* ROSEN.)

ROSEN. Good God, what now ?

DR. HAGGETT. Come in here, all of you ! Never mind the
portrait ! The other pictures have been found !

TALLANT. No !

(GWENNY *listens in confusion and alarm.*)

DR. HAGGETT. The ones that you burnt, Hannah ! (*He hugs
her.*)

MRS. HAGGETT. Arthur ! (*She embraces* DR. HAGGETT.)

DR. HAGGETT (*laughing*). Only you never burnt them ! Gwenny's
got them in her box ! Seventeen of them !

DAVENPORT. Seventeen new Christopher Beans !

(GWENNY *moves up to below the fireplace.* BRUCE MCRAE *comes in to the hall from* R., *carrying* GWENNY'S *old leather trunk tied up with rope.* SUSAN *follows to steer it clear of the paint.*)

MRS. HAGGETT. Arthur, it's a fortune!

ADA. And it is ours! And it's ours!

DR. HAGGETT (*breaking loose from the women*). Put that box down and open it! (*He charges into the hall.*)

BRUCE (*stopping*). But I just tied all this rope round it——

DR. HAGGETT. Then untie the rope again! Cut it! You've got a knife, haven't you?

(BRUCE *puts down the box, takes out a knife and bends over the trunk; the others all move up closer to the trunk.*)

GWENNY (*crossing to* DR. HAGGETT). Oh, Doctor Haggett, you will make me lose my train——

ADA. Talking about trains at a time like this!

BRUCE (*cutting the rope*). There ye are, Doctor!

(DR. HAGGETT *throws up the lid of the box.*)

DR. HAGGETT. Now, Gwenny, where are they?

GWENNY (*going up to the trunk*). Better let me do it, Doctor Haggett. I do not like people to be rummaging and messing in my box.

(*There is a silence. She bends over the box and takes out a fattish roll of canvases bound with string, from beneath several articles of wearing apparel.*)

DR. HAGGETT. Hah!

(*He snatches them from her and comes down to* ROSEN, *who is by the chair* L. *of the table.*)

Now I'll talk business with you, Mr. Rosen.

ROSEN. Excuse me, Doctor Haggett, but I'm the picture dealer.

(*He takes the pictures from* DR. HAGGETT, *turns and crosses to the desk, sits in the chair, places the paintings on the desk and unrolls them.* DR. HAGGETT *crosses to above the desk.* MRS. HAGGETT *follows to below the desk.* ADA *above desk to* L. *of it.* TALLANT *moves to below the armchair.*)

Well, Doctor Haggett, I wasn't prepared for a deal like this!

DAVENPORT. Carefully now! (*He crosses to* R. *of* DR. HAGGETT *and peers over his shoulder.*) Don't harm them! . . . (*As the roll opens out flat.*) Ah!

DR. HAGGETT. What do you think it's worth?

DAVENPORT. Well, now, I don't know——

GWENNY (*to* BRUCE). Will you tie the rope round my box again for me, Bruce, there iss a nice boy, yes?

(BRUCE *ropes up the box,* SUSAN *helping him.* GWENNY *looks from the box to the group at the desk, undetermined.*)

DR. HAGGETT. What would you say it's worth, Mr. Davenport ? You said you'd tell me. Is it worth two thousand ?

DAVENPORT. Easily, I should say.

DR. HAGGETT (*wildly excited*). Do you hear that, Hannah ? Easily two thousand, for the first one on the pile ! And seventeen of them !

ADA (*coming down and putting her arm about* MRS. HAGGETT). We're rich, Mummy ! Rich !

(ROSEN *turns over a new picture.*)

DAVENPORT. Oh !

MRS. HAGGETT (*sitting on the chair below the desk*). Yes, it does look as if we're rich, and I think it's having an effect on my stomach.

(*During the following scene,* GWENNY *makes repeated attempts to interrupt the proceedings at the desk, but her every effort to attract their attention is drowned in an outburst from them. Their attitude is one of complete indifference to her presence ; and they pay no heed to her pitiful attempts to edge in.*)

GWENNY (*crossing down to* R. *of the desk*). Were you planning on selling those too, Doctor Haggett ?

(TALLANT *turns and looks at his own painting by the cabinet.*)

DR. HAGGETT. What's this one ?

DAVENPORT (*bending over the second canvas*). " The Briar Turnpike Cornfield." It must be " The Briar Turnpike Cornfield " !

(TALLANT *turns and looks at* DAVENPORT *in dismay, from just* R. *of him.*)

DR. HAGGETT. Certainly it's " The Briar Turnpike Cornfield " !

(TALLANT *looks at the picture, crosses to his own at the medical cabinet, picks it up and exits* C.)

GWENNY. I saved those—— (*She stops as she sees* TALLANT *disappearing.*)

DR. HAGGETT. I used to go courting through it, I ought to know.

(*There is a pause.*)

DAVENPORT (*as he sees another painting*). Oh, look !

GWENNY. I—I saved those from burning, and I wass thinking they wass mine for keeps !

ROSEN (*to* DR. HAGGETT). Now, look here, Doctor Haggett, before we start talking business, I must know if you really are the rightful owner this time.

MRS. HAGGETT. Who would be, if my husband isn't ?

Dr. Haggett. I've got your word for it they belong to me. And weren't they left here as a security for a bill that was never paid?

Davenport. Yes, Rosen, I expect they do belong to him.

Gwenny. Oh!

Dr. Haggett. There you are, you see!

Gwenny. Well . . .

Davenport. Let's look through the rest.

(*Nobody pays the slightest heed to* Gwenny.)

Rosen (*seated in the swivel chair*). Well, as I say, I never tackled anything as big as this before. A corner in Christopher Beans! By Jove!

Gwenny. Well . . . Good afternoon, all. I will be going off now.

Dr. Haggett. That's what it is, Mr. Rosen. (*With a laugh.*) A corner!

Gwenny. My train will be going, Doctor Haggett—that's why I——

Davenport. I wouldn't be in a hurry to sell, Doctor. Not the lot, anyway.

Rosen. I wasn't prepared for that, Mr. Davenport.

Gwenny. Good-bye, Ada. Good-bye, Mrs. Haggett!

Rosen. Why, he may have forty thousand pounds' worth of stuff in this little lot!

Ada. Oh, Mummy!

Rosen (*pounding the top of the desk with his fist*). I don't know, though. I might get the deal financed. Would you give me time?

Dr. Haggett. I don't know about giving time, I'm sure . . .

Gwenny. Well, ta-ta . . . Well . . . (*She turns back to* Bruce *with a pathetic little laugh.*) I think I better just go.

Rosen (*to himself*). Blauberg might come in on this . . . and there's Goldstein, I might put him down for a . . .

(*The group at the desk turn over another picture, and another, with low exclamations of delighted amazement.*)

Gwenny. Will you take my box out, Bruce?

(Bruce *nods to* Susan, *who goes out through the front door.* Bruce *follows and goes out of the front door which he leaves open.* Gwenny *picks up her suitcase by the door* R., *and stands for a moment, looking around her.*)

Rosen. I tell you what, Doctor Haggett. Suppose you keep that cheque for a thirty-day option?

Dr. Haggett. Well, if you put a price on the lot now. But a good price, mind.

ROSEN. Let me work it out.

(DAVENPORT, *losing interest in the bargaining, turns away from the group at the desk and sees* GWENNY *picking up her suitcase.*)

DR. HAGGETT (*with a laugh*). You fire away, Mr. Rosen, we aren't going to interfere with you working it out!

(ROSEN *proceeds to do so, all the others watching over his shoulder.* GWENNY *returns to above the portrait.*)

DAVENPORT. Oh, Gwenny! (*He goes to* L. *of her.*) You're not going, are you?

(*She stoops and puts her suitcase down in front of her portrait.*)

GWENNY. Yes, I am going, Mistar Davenport. I try to say good-bye, but, duweed, they are so busy!

DAVENPORT. Will you let me say just one word to you about your portrait? Oh, I'm not trying to take it away from you! But, Gwenny, a work of art like that is a responsibility. It's yours, but only yours in trust for the future. Take it with you to Manchester, by all means. But when you get there, don't keep it where it won't be safe. Lend it to the City Art Gallery. You could go there and see it every day, you know. Would you do that, Gwenny?

GWENNY. I would think about it, Mistar Davenport.

ROSEN (*looking up from his figures*). Thirty-five thousand pounds.

DR. HAGGETT. You said forty thousand!

(ROSEN *turns to* DAVENPORT. DR. HAGGETT *also turns to face* DAVENPORT, *who holds up his hand for silence.* MRS. HAGGETT *looks up, and rises.*)

DAVENPORT. Please, Gwenny! I know it's more than a work of art to you. I know the bond that must have existed between you and Chris Bean when he painted it.

MRS. HAGGETT (*with a supercilious sniff*). Bond, indeed! Huh! Carryings-on! If you can call that a bond!

(GWENNY *looks at her, but turns back with her own dignity to answer* DAVENPORT.)

GWENNY. Mistar Davenport, he wass the only man that ever ask me to marry him.

(*Though the words are spoken shyly, they fall like lead on the room's sudden attention. There is a pause.*)

DR. HAGGETT (*all but speechless*). You . . . (*Moving towards her.*) You didn't marry him, though, Gwenny?

(Mrs. Haggett *moves a step* R., *still below the desk.* Ada *comes round to below the desk.*)

Gwenny. He wass so ill, that I could not say no to nothing that he asked from me.

(*The idea strikes all present simultaneously.*)

Davenport (*with pleased surprise*). Then you're his widow ?

(Rosen *rolls up the paintings.*)

Gwenny. I know that I am.

(*There is a pause.*)

Rosen. Then these pictures belong to her——

(Bruce *comes back, takes the portrait and the suitcase and goes out again. All of the following speeches are spoken simultaneously.*)

Dr. Haggett (*shaking his head*). She's got to prove it ! She's got to prove it ! She's got to prove it !

Davenport (*to him*). I believe she can ! I certainly believe she can ! (*To* Gwenny.) And you never told ! But, Gwenny, why didn't you ? . . . This is magnificent ! And it's certainly turning out the way Chris would have——

Rosen (*to* Mrs. Haggett). My God, I can't do business this way ! If they don't know the difference between——

(Mrs. Haggett *tears the roll of paintings out of his hands.*)

Well, I give it up !

Mrs. Haggett (*clasping the paintings tightly in her arms*). Well, she doesn't get them away from me ! Not over my dead body, she doesn't—if these pictures were mine to burn, they're mine to keep !

Ada. Mummy ! Does that mean that Daddy can't . . . Mummy, answer me ! Aren't these pictures ours to sell ? Oh, it isn't fair ! It isn't fair, really. . . . I don't think it is——

Gwenny (*to one after the other, and to all at once*). Certainly I can prove it. I got my marriage lines out in my—— (*She points to the front door, through which* Bruce *has taken her trunk.*) Do you want to see . . . And my wedding-ring on a—— (*She pulls out her wedding-ring, on a ribbon, from her bosom.*) Look you !

(Dr. Haggett *throws up his hands in defeat, turns, and goes towards* Mrs. Haggett. Gwenny *follows down a few steps after him.* Davenport *moves to the back of the armchair.*)

I wass wanting people to have a good idear of me, like . . . but I do not care who knows it now, that I am Mrs. Christopher Bean

—that iss who I am, just the same ass Mrs. Haggett iss Mrs. Haggett——

(DR. HAGGETT *tears the roll of paintings away from his wife, turns, and goes to* GWENNY.)

And I never have no carryings-on, nor——

(DR. HAGGETT *hands the paintings to her. The* CURTAIN *begins to fall as* GWENNY *exits* C.)

CURTAIN.

FURNITURE AND PROPERTY PLOT

ACT I

On Stage.

Old-fashioned carpet all over.
Fireplace up R.C.—Fire logs (not practical).
Pair of brass andirons.
Mantelpiece.—Imitation marble clock.
Ashtray and matches.
Flower-vase with flowers.
2 Ornaments.
Spill-holder with spills.
Old round dining-table R.C.—White felt table-cloth (tacked on).
Tapestry table-cloth.
Bowl of flowers.
Copy of local newspaper.
Telegram in envelope.
Old-fashioned sideboard against the wall R.
On top: White linen runner.
Old silver pitcher.
Old silver dish with cover.
Old pewter tea-pot.
In top drawer upstage end of sideboard: 4 Knives.
4 Forks.
4 Soup-spoons.
4 Tea-spoons.
In top drawer downstage end of sideboard: Folded yellow check table-cloth.
4 White napkins in rings.
In sideboard cupboard: Cruet.
Marmalade.
Knee-hole desk L.—Tooled leather desk set.
Large blotter.
Hand-blotter.
Loose papers.
Several cancelled and opened envelopes.
Large white pad.
Cash-book with entries.
3 Medical books.
Microscope.
Small rack of test-tubes.
2 Large test-tubes, 1 small test-tube.
2 Large medical bottles with name written on each.
Round glass jar with pieces of gauze.
Pens and pencils.
Ashtray and matches.
Desk-lamp with emerald shade (not practical).
Telephone.
Small telephone-book.
Tobacco-jar.

Telegram planted under papers.

Small appointment book, another in top drawer.

Medical cabinet L. of fireplace.

On top : Ashtray filled with cigarette-ends.

3 Medical bottles with name written on each.

In medical cabinet : Thin transparent curtain.

Several medical bottles.

Corner cabinet up L.C.

On top : World globe.

On shelves : Several china ornaments.

Blue cobalt platter, propped up.

4 Victorian chairs set round the table.

1 Chair to match below the door R., another in upstage L. corner.

Victorian sidechair below the desk L.

Victorian armchair L.C.

Victorian stool below the medical cabinet.

Victorian leather-covered swivel chair R. of the desk.

Aspidistra on stand in bay window.

Fire-log carrier just L. of fireplace.

Red plush footstool just R. of fireplace.

3 Pairs of white window curtains at bay-window L.

1 Pair of white window curtains at window above desk.

1 Pair of tapestry drapes on rod at bay-window.

Oval rag rug tacked down by door R.

Rag rug tacked down below double doors C.

Rag rug tacked down below the fireplace.

Framed oil-painting of buttercup flowers in vase, on wall over mantel.

Framed etching on flat over door R.

Framed oil-painting of dog's head on flat up L.C.

Framed old-fashioned photograph of woman, on flat above bay-windows.

Calendar on wall above medical cabinet.

In Hallway.—Table, not to be seen, just off L.

Old used step-ladder placed against stair newel-post.

Old strip of canvas with paint stains hanging from ladder.

2 Paint-cans, with several brushes in each, just out of sight off R.

" Wet Paint " notice hanging on stair newel-post.

Off stage L.

For DR. HAGGETT.—Doctor's black leather bag.

Old pipe.

Rubber tobacco-pouch.

Pocket-watch on chain.

Pair of spectacles.

For TALLANT.—4 Five-pound notes.

More than 12 one-pound notes.

More than 1 ten-shilling note.

More than two shillings in silver.

Off stage R.

For GWENNY.—Wooden tray, on which : Tea-pot, filled.

Cup and saucer.

Milk and sugar-bowls.

Folded napkin in ring.

Small plate.

Dessert-spoon, tea-spoon, knife.

Tin tray, on which : Plate of porridge.

Butter-dish.

Toast in rack.

Hot-water jug.

Sugar-sifter with sugar.

Old iron kettle.

For BRUCE.—2 Small framed oil-paintings.
For MRS. HAGGETT.—Old dirty square of canvas.

ACT II

The same as Act I.
    Strike.—Newspaper on mantelpiece.
           Piece of paper on table.
    On sideboard.—4 Dinner-plates.
               4 Soup-plates.
               4 Glass tumblers.
               Jug of water.
               Cruet.
               Platter with loaf of bread and bread-knife.
Off stage L.
    For ROSEN.—Cigarette-case (filled).
               Cigarette-lighter.
               Visiting-card.
               Cheque and cheque-book.
               Legal papers, bill of sale.
               Fountain-pen.
    For DR. HAGGETT.—Black leather bag.
Off stage R.
    For DAVENPORT.—Copy of the " London Mercury."
    For GWENNY.—Telegram in envelope.
               Soup-tureen with soup and ladle.

ACT III

The same as Act I.
    Strike.—Books, telephone-book and 2 medical bottles from desk
    Set.—7 telegrams on desk.
Off stage L.
    For TALLANT.—Unframed oil-painting.
Off stage R.
    For GWENNY.—Glass of milk and plate of biscuits.
               Large unframed oil-painting.
               Large frame for portrait.
               Ladies' suitcase.
               Wedding-ring on ribbon.
    For BRUCE.—Small old leather trunk, tied up with rope.
               In trunk : Roll of oil-painted canvases.
                     Several articles of wearing apparel.
               Pocket-knife.
    For DR. HAGGETT.—More than 10 one-pound notes.
    For ROSEN.—Cheque-book.
               Fountain-pen.
               Bill of sale.
    For DAVENPORT.—Hat and coat on table off L. in hall.
    For SUSAN.—Hat and coat on table off L. in hall.

EFFECTS

Clock-strike, up R. corner behind fireplace.
Door-bell on front door.
Telephone-bell, behind drapes on window.

PERISHABLES

Porridge, butter, bread, sugar, milk, tea, cruet, marmalade, soup and biscuits.